Civil Engineering Heritage

W. A. Fairhurst & Partners

The Tyne bridges at Newcastle

Civil Engineering Heritage

NORTHERN ENGLAND

M. F. Barbey

CEng FICE

THOMAS TELFORD LIMITED

LONDON 1981

iv

First published 1981
by Thomas Telford Limited, PO Box 101, 26–34 Old Street, London EC1P 1JH
for the Institution of Civil Engineers

ISBN: 0 7277 0098 7

Thomas Telford Limited as a body does not accept responsibility for the statements made or the opinions expressed in the following pages.

Set and printed by Henry Ling Ltd, Dorchester, and bound by Leighton Straker, London.

PANEL FOR HISTORICAL ENGINEERING WORKS
J.W. Baxter (Chairman); Lt Col. R.H. Edwards (Deputy Chairman);
M.F. Barbey (Technical Secretary); T.B. O'Loughlin (Assistant
Technical Secretary); D.J. Adler, A.G. Allnutt, A.E. Butcher, R.
Cragg, P. Dunkerley, J.K. Gardiner, A.B. George, O.M. Gibbs, R.V.
Hughes, J. McClure, T.R. Mills, R.A. Paxton, R.M. Phelps, R.W.
Rennison, W.J. Sivewright, A. Turner, H.S. Waddington

Foreword

THIS book is based on the work of The Panel for Historical Engineering Works of the Institution of Civil Engineers and has been organised by the Panel's Technical Secretary, Mr M.F. Barbey, acting in the capacity of editor and principal author.

The Panel for Historical Engineering Works has built up a considerable library of records of civil engineering works of interest. These records list all ascertainable pertinent facts about each item and constitute a valuable reference facility in a field in which interest is increasing.

Interest is growing not only among civil engineers but generally, and the Panel decided to make some of its information available to the public in the belief that many people would welcome a concise readable account of engineering works of historical importance in their own areas and any they may visit.

This volume covers the northern area of England but it is hoped that as the Panel's work continues further volumes will appear so that eventually the whole of the country will be covered.

We have a rich engineering heritage and the Panel hopes that fostering interest in historical works will strengthen resistance to their destruction. So often valuable items are demolished because their true worth and rarity is appreciated by so few people.

Thanks are due to the Panel members and their associates chiefly concerned, particularly, in addition to Mr Barbey, Messrs R.A. Paxton, R.W. Rennison, P. Dunkerley and R.V. Hughes. Mr T.B. O'Loughlin undertook extensive checking and correcting. Thanks are also due to the staff of British Rail, British Waterways, local authorities, public utilities and others for their help and encouragement, and to the Ordnance Survey for permission to reproduce the grid references.

J.W. BAXTER
Chairman, Panel for Historical Engineering Works; Past President, Institution of Civil Engineers

Metric equivalents

Throughout this book, Imperial measurements have been used in giving dimensions of the works described, as this system was used in the design of the great majority.

The following are metric equivalents of the Imperial units used.

Length
1 inch = 25.4 millimetres
1 foot = 0.3048 metres
1 yard = 0.9144 metres
1 chain = 20.12 metres
1 furlong = 201.2 metres
1 mile = 1.609 kilometres

Area
1 acre = 0.4047 hectares

Volume
1 gallon = 4.546 litres
1 cubic yard = 0.7617 cubic metres

Flow rate
1000 gallons per hour = 1.263 litres per second
100 gallons per minute = 7.577 litres per second

Mass
1 pound = 0.4536 kilogram
1 imperial ton = 1.016 tonne

Mass/ length
1 pound per yard = 0.496 kilograms per metre

Power
1 horse power = 0.7457 kilowatt

Pressure
1 pound force per square inch = 0.06895 bar.

Contents

Introduction

In 1971 the Institution of Civil Engineers set up the Panel for Historical Engineering Works. Mr R.W. Hawkey, a Member of Council of the Institution, became the first Chairman and laid down the guidelines which govern the Panel's operations. The main object is to locate and record suitable items in all fields of civil engineering activity. Not all items are recorded but selected ones, large or small, famous or little known, which exemplify some particular stage in engineering development.

Civil engineering is usually concerned with large-scale projects and bulk materials handling, with heavy static loads or applied dynamic loads. Domestic and commercial building on a modest scale does not generally involve civil engineering beyond a little consultation. Quite a small proportion (less than 15%) of the items in a book on industrial archaeology is likely to lie within the Panel's field of interest. The process of locating, researching and recording an item for inclusion in the Panel's register can be quite lengthy and a final decision on whether an item should be fully recorded has to wait until the investigations are in an advanced stage.

The more notable works by Telford, Rennie, Brunel, Stephenson and other famous civil engineers are naturally included. The aim however is to present a much wider view of civil engineers' achievements by means of a large number of lesser known works. All of them, however small, are either very attractive or have some special point of technical interest for anyone wishing to understand by example what the profession has done over the years for the environment, the economy, and for the use and convenience of man.

The book is divided into areas, giving a group of works which can all be easily visited from a central point. Within each area they are dealt with so as to provide some idea of the scope and development of civil engineering within that region, rather than as

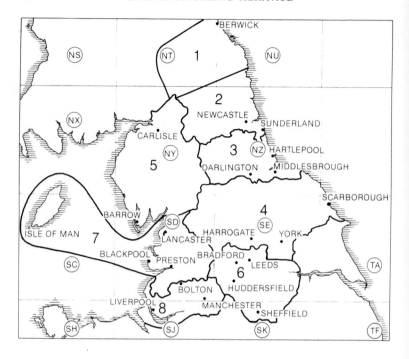

a gazetteer or list of statistics, and the order of the items within each area arises from this consideration.

Each chapter contains a map giving the location of the works described, a brief history of engineering developments within that particular area, and information on the individual works. Ordnance Survey grid references are given for each item, as is also the HEW (Historical Engineering Work) number, that is the number under which the work is registered in the records in the Library of the Institution of Civil Engineers.

The material within the book has been collated from much fuller and more detailed technical records both of the works described and of other HEWs or potential HEWs in the north of England. The Panel's work is a continuing process, and other works which have been registered or are under current investigation are listed at the end of the book. In addition to references to specific works (indicated by superior numerals in the text), a bibliography of books dealing more broadly with the civil engineering history of the area or of particular types of structure is included. However, the selection has been made with a view to providing both civil engineers and the general reader with some idea of the immense variety and expertise which comprise our civil engineering heritage.

CHAPTER 1

The Border

NORTH of Hadrian's Wall, the border between England and
Scotland runs north east from Carlisle to Berwick-upon-Tweed. In
addition to the several main roads to Edinburgh, important routes
run from west to east, serving Berwick, once a port of considerable
standing. In more recent times, in the railway era, another major

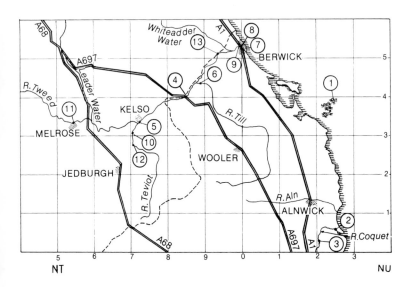

1. Longstone Lighthouse	8. Royal Tweed Bridge
2. Warkworth Bridge	9. Royal Border Bridge
3. Acklington Mill Weir	10. Roxburgh Viaduct footbridge
4. Coldstream Bridge	11. Gattonside suspension footbridge,
5. Kelso Bridge	Melrose
6. Twizel Bridge	12. Kalemouth suspension bridge
7. Berwick Bridge	13. Union Bridge

north-south link emerged, now forming the present east coast main line of British Railways.

This is clearly a district in which one might expect to find as good a miscellany of historic bridges by several of the greatest of British engineers as anywhere in the country; indeed this is so. Outstanding examples of the work of Smeaton, Rennie, Robert Stephenson and Samuel Brown are sandwiched between both earlier and later bridges, themselves of no mean order. Berwick-upon-Tweed itself has a set of three, and could well achieve a fourth if the present by-pass scheme comes to fruition. The town is historically unique in two or three other ways, and there is much of interest to see both in and around it.

1. Longstone Lighthouse   (HEW 699)   NU 246 390

The Farne Islands, lying between 1½ and 5¼ miles off the coast of Northumberland, vary in number from 28 at low water to 15 at high water. The two main islands are Inner Farne and Staple, the homes of large breeding colonies of sea birds. The Longstone Lighthouse is situated at the north-east tip of the Farnes and is one of two in use today, the other being at the landward end of Farne itself.

The Longstone Lighthouse is a red and white tower with a light some 85 ft high and it is listed as a building of historic interest. It was completed in 1826 and, following damage during the 1939–45 war, was repaired in 1952. Before its construction there were lights somewhat in-shore, on Staple, Pinnacle Island and on Bronnsman; parts of these structures are still used by birdwatchers.

The Lighthouse on Farne Island is historically of some interest in that in 1669 Sir John Clayton built a tower as a speculative venture although it was not used. Trinity House obtained a Patent in 1776 and it is thought that the present lantern murette, which is unique, dates from that time, although the building was constructed (or reconstructed) about 1811. The history of the Longstone Lighthouse is now inextricably mixed with the story of Grace Darling who, with her father, was responsible for rescuing survivors from the wreck of the paddle steamer *Forfarshire*. Bound from Hull to Dundee with 64 passengers and crew, the ship was wrecked in September 1838. The Grace Darling Museum in Bamburgh is open to visitors from June to September.

2. Warkworth Bridge   (HEW 696)   NU 249 062

A different kind of tower, but none the less interesting, may be
seen at Warkworth, some 20 miles to the south. It is a mediaeval
defensive work at one end of the 14th century bridge over the
Coquet. The similar but more famous Monnow bridge at
Monmouth has the tower actually on the bridge. Warkworth has
two segmental four-ribbed arches of about 60 ft span, with a
massive cutwater on the central pier. It formerly carried the A1068
road over the river Coquet but is now restricted to pedestrian
traffic, principally because of its extremely narrow width.

3. Acklington Mill Weir   (HEW 396)   NU 202 029
Figure 1/1

Also on the river Coquet in Northumberland stands a masonry

Figure 1/1. Acklington Mill Weir

weir or dam unusual in that its downstream face is vertical. The dam was built in 1776 by John Smeaton to provide a source of power for a local iron works and it is curved in plan, to a radius of 170 ft, supported by masonry abutments on the river banks 142 ft apart. The dam is 8 ft high and its base is 8 ft wide, a feature of its construction being the fact that the river was diverted through the abutments in conduits 2 ft square provided for this purpose.[1]

4. Coldstream Bridge   (HEW 158)   NT 849 401   Figure 1/2

In 1766 a bridge designed by John Smeaton was opened to carry traffic over the river Tweed between Coldstream and Cornhill. The masonry bridge comprises five main arches, all approximating to 60 ft span, and there is a further dry arch at each end. The bridge piers were founded, where necessary, on piles and have had to be protected by concrete 'starlings' to reduce scour, and a dam was built downstream further to reduce the problem. The arches of the bridge are segmental and the spandrels are perforated to reduce the loading on the foundations, although the apertures are filled at the bridge faces. Originally 22 ft in width, the bridge was widened in 1960 by the addition of cantilevered reinforced concrete footways.[2]

5. Kelso Bridge   (HEW 308)   NT 727 336

Of John Rennie's bridge over the river Tweed at Kelso, Samuel Smiles, biographer of the country's leading engineers, wrote that 'it was long regarded as one of the most handsome and effective structures of its kind', a view not disputed a century later.

The masonry bridge comprises five semi-elliptical arches, each spanning 72 ft, and the piers, 12 ft thick, are decorated with Doric pilasters; the bridge carries a level roadway 23 ft 6 in wide and a toll house still stands at its north end. In form similar to the now demolished Waterloo Bridge, London, the bridge was opened in 1803.

6. Twizel Bridge   (HEW 90)   NT 885 434   Figure 1/3

Between Berwick and Cornhill, the river Till is crossed by a mediaeval stone bridge at Twizel. This elegant bridge has a span of 90 ft—at the time of its construction the greatest of any such bridge in England—and the slightly pointed arch incorporates five narrow

Figure 1/2. Coldstream Bridge (J.M. Gibson)

Figure 1/3. Twizel Bridge

chamfered ribs. The rise of the arch is 40 ft. It is known that it was used by troops on the way to the fighting at Flodden in 1513 but its date of construction is not known, although it may be as early as the 14th century.

7. Berwick Bridge, Berwick-upon-Tweed   (HEW 694)
NT 996 527

Of the hundreds of early road bridges in Britain this is one of the larger and more important. It was built between 1611 and 1624 and carried the London–Edinburgh–Thurso trunk road over the Tweed until 1928, when increasing traffic forced the provision of the adjacent four-span reinforced concrete arch bridge.

It is significant that the vast and unique fortifications at Berwick had scarcely been completed by Queen Elizabeth when James VI of Scotland became also James I of England, making them redundant, and improved communications became the more important policy. In fact it is said that James, heading south for London, was so alarmed by the condition of the then existing timber bridge that he gave personal instructions for its replacement.

From water level the bridge indeed gives the impression of size and strength. It has 15 rather large semi-circular (slightly pointed) arches increasing in height to a maximum towards the Berwick town end; the longest span is 75 ft. There are 14 pairs of cutwater/pier/refuges making a length approaching ¼ mile.

8. Royal Tweed Bridge   (HEW 695)   NT 995 528
Figure 1/4

This very striking four-arch reinforced concrete bridge replaced the old masonry bridge in 1928 as the major route to the north via Berwick-upon-Tweed. There is a rising gradient towards the town so that the four-rib segmental arches increase in span from 167 ft to 248, 285 and 361 ft 5 in, the last being then the largest reinforced concrete arch in Britain. The bridge was designed by L. G. Mouchel and Partners.

9. Royal Border Bridge   (HEW 20)   NT 993 533   Figure 1/5

Together with the crossing of the Tyne at Newcastle, the Royal Border Bridge over the river Tweed at Berwick removed the major obstacles to completion of the east coast route of railway from London to Edinburgh. The Newcastle and Berwick Railway Company had been formed in 1845 and, with Robert Stephenson as its Engineer, began the construction of the line almost immediately. The viaduct at Berwick is built on a curve and consists of 28 arches, each of 61 ft 6 in span; the rails are at a level of 120 ft above the river. The structure has a total length of 2160 ft and the arches comprise two sets of 14 each with a stop pier between them; the arches have brick soffits while the faces of the piers are of masonry.

As with the High Level Bridge at Newcastle, Stephenson was associated with T.E. Harrison, later to be Engineer to the North

Figure 1/4. Royal Tweed Bridge, Berwick

Figure 1/5. Royal Border Bridge, Berwick

Eastern Railway, while the Resident Engineer was (Sir) George B. Bruce; contractors were James McKay and J. Blastock.[3] The bridge was opened by Queen Victoria on 29 August 1850.

10. Roxburgh Viaduct footbridge   (HEW 402)
NT 702 304   Figure 1/6

Bridges with lenticular trusses are rather rare: the three included in this book are that near Bishop Auckland (HEW 307 in Chapter 3) which has one span; this bridge at Roxburgh with three spans, and the Gaunless Bridge (HEW 190 in Chapter 4), now at York, which has four.

The river Teviot runs northwards from Jedburgh to the Tweed and the North British Railway crossed it just east of Roxburgh on a beautifully built stone viaduct constructed in 1850. The river itself is spanned by three arches whose pier bases are extended on the downstream side to carry a three-span footbridge. This has a timber floor 5 ft wide which undulates because of the lenticular shape of the 50 ft trusses, which have a maximum depth at centre of about 4 ft. The top chord is flat cast iron 5 in by 1 in on edge

Figure 1/6. Roxburgh Viaduct footbridge

and the bottom chord is 1½ in diameter wrought iron bar, jointed at the middle. The chords are strutted apart by five V-shaped cast iron frames with decreasing circular motifs; these frames are forked top and bottom around the chords, bolted at the top and cross-tied at the bottom. The deck is 6 in by 3 in timber and the parapets have eleven panels of very light iron rod in a Union Jack pattern about 5 ft by 3 ft. The parapet was raised with light channel iron rails at some later date.

11. Gattonside suspension footbridge, Melrose (HEW 409)
NT 545 346
The lower Tweed Valley is rich in early suspension bridges, this one being a footbridge of 300 ft span. It was constructed by

Redpath Brown and Co. of Edinburgh, opened on 26 October 1826 and overhauled by them in 1928.[4] Being only 4 ft 6 in wide with very light components and no stiffening, it is a very mobile bridge under load.

The towers are monumental, in a Victorian Gothic style, 24 ft above road level. The chains are of 1¾ in diameter rod 10 ft long with forged ends, four in all, that is two pairs. The hangers are ¾ in diameter spaced at 9 ft 9 in centres and there are light iron post and rail parapets. The sag of the chain is 17 ft and the rise of the deck (which is timber) is 3 ft. The bridge is some distance outside Melrose itself to the north west.

12. Kalemouth suspension bridge   (HEW 410)   NT 708 274

The Tweed flows eastward from Melrose to Kelso where it is joined from the south by the Teviot. Halfway to Jedburgh the Kalewater meets the Teviot from the east near Eckford and this bridge is over the Teviot near the confluence. It carries a minor road and has a span of 180 ft. It is 16 ft wide overall, 14 ft between chains, 10 ft 8 in between kerbs and 8 ft 8 in between pillars. Not only the road width but also the permissible load is restricted.

There are four rather crude pyramidal pylons 16 ft high and the chains and hangers are similar those of the bridge at Melrose (HEW 409) with a sag of 13 ft on the smaller span. The parapets however are a heavy timber lattice in 5 ft by 3 ft panels with diagonals. The timber deck has the upper planks crosswise.

The bridge was designed by Captain Sir Samuel Brown RN who also supplied the ironwork, presumably from the Brown Lennox chain works, which I. K. Brunel later patronised; William Mather, a local contractor, was responsible for the masonry. It seems that the precise date of building is unknown but it would be in the period 1820–30.

13. Union Bridge   (HEW 143)   NT 934 511   Figure 1/7

In 1817 Captain (later Sir) Samuel Brown obtained a patent for wrought iron cable chain links, at the same time constructing a model suspension bridge at his works. Subsequently he was responsible for the construction of the Brighton Chain Pier and for many suspension bridges now demolished. The Union Bridge, crossing the river Tweed some five miles west of Berwick, stands as a memorial to his work, being the earliest surviving road suspension

Figure 1/7. Union Bridge: (above) from south west; (below) north cable anchorage

bridge in Britain. In its day it was said to be the longest in the world.

With a span of 361 ft, twelve wrought iron chains carry a road deck 18 ft in width and the bridge is unusual, if not unique, in that it has only one stone pylon 60 ft high, there being no such feature on the south bank, where the cables are anchored directly to the rock face at about the level of the top of the north tower.

Including the approaches, the total length of the bridge is some 600 ft, and with the tollhouse at its north end it was opened in July 1820. It should, however, be pointed out that the bridge was strengthened by the addition of steel cables in 1903.[5]

CHAPTER 2

Tyne and Wear

SINCE the 13th century coal has been mined along the banks of the rivers Tyne and Wear, initially obtained from out-cropping seams and then by shallow mining. The invention of the steam engine resulted in the easier working of deeper pits. It was principally from the coal industry that the region's first civil engineers came, among them George Stephenson, and it was under a committee of mining engineers that the Newcastle and Carlisle Railway, originally conceived as a canal, was completed.

Associated with the growth of the railways was the construction of several notable bridges, among them Robert Stephenson's High Level Bridge on the Tyne, and the Victoria Viaduct crossing the Wear. Significant advances were also made in the use of iron in, for example, the roof of Newcastle's Central Station and in the early fixed arch bridge crossing the Tyne at Wylam. With the railways, too, came the construction of docks and staithes, facilities promoted both by the railways and by the Commissioners of the two rivers. The latter were responsible for the improvements which took place on both Tyne and Wear, mainly in the latter part of the 19th century when extensive dredging and the construction of piers were undertaken.

As the area's population increased, so did the needs of the inhabitants. On a small scale water had been supplied by speculators in Newcastle from 1680 but in 1832 a joint stock Company was formed, the forerunner of the Newcastle and Gateshead Water Company; in a like manner the Sunderland and South Shields Company was formed by amalgamation in 1852. Sewerage was the responsibility of local government, but gas and electricity were, from 1817 and 1880 respectively, supplied by efficient and enterprising companies.

The 20th century brought to Tyneside several early reinforced concrete buildings, still to be seen. The development of this form

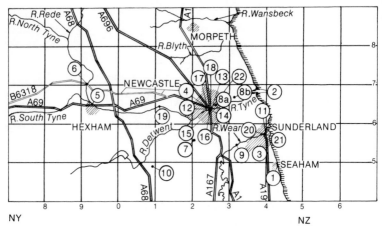

NY

NZ

1. Seaham Harbour
2. Tyne Piers
3. Ryhope Pumping Station
4. Newcastle-Carlisle Road
5. Hexham Bridge, Northumberland
6. Roman bridges, Chollerford
7. Causey Arch, Tanfield
8a. Ouseburn Viaduct
8b. Willington Viaduct
9. Victoria Viaduct, Penshaw
10. Hownes Gill Viaduct
11. Monkwearmouth Station
12. Newcastle Central Station

13. Dean Street arch bridge, Newcastle
14. No. 5 Bridge, Newcastle
15. High Level Bridge, Newcastle
16. King Edward VII railway Bridge, Newcastle
17. Newcastle Swing Bridge
18. Tyne Bridge, Newcastle
19. Wrought iron arch bridge, Wylam
20. Wearmouth Bridge, Sunderland
21. Wear Bridge, Sunderland
22. Reinforced concrete warehouse, Newcastle.

of construction by Hennebique had led to his methods being adopted by Mouchel, who established an office in Newcastle, following which several early structures were erected. Prior to Hennebique's work, however, a patent for reinforced concrete had been obtained by W.B. Wilkinson of Newcastle and a building incorporating his principles was actually built by him in 1865. A relic from this is preserved in the Library of the Institution of Civil Engineers in Westminster.

1. Seaham Harbour   (HEW 758)   NZ 43 49
Lord Londonderry served with Wellington at Waterloo and was later the British Ambassador in Vienna. He acquired the Seaham Estate in 1821 and from that time the mining of coal there was

greatly extended.[1] The coal was at first shipped from Sunderland, but Londonderry proposed that a new port should be made at Seaham and plans were prepared by William Chapman. An Act of Parliament was obtained and work started in 1828 by direct labour under Chapman and John Buddle (Lord Londonderry's Viewer). The construction of the harbour and its associated railway was completed in 1831, while some four years later the port was extended by the building of the South Dock. The North Dock was extended in 1844, and a second railway was built from Seaham to Sunderland in 1854, allowing coal to be exported from the Wear also. Built originally as a private venture the port was taken into the care of the Seaham Harbour Dock Company, formed in 1898, following which the docks were enlarged and new piers built.[2]

2. Tyne Piers (HEW 759) NZ 375 693 and 374 678
Figure 2/1

For at least a hundred years before the coming of railways, coal was exported in quantity from numerous piers, jetties, and drops along the River Tyne. Much of it went to London and gave rise to the expression 'coals to Newcastle'—meaning it was the height of absurdity even to think of the traffic flowing in that direction.

A vast network of waggonways, mostly narrow gauge and with wooden rails, brought the coal from the pits down to the ships. Horse power and falling gradients enabled chaldrons of about two tons capacity to be moved.

The coming of steam locomotives, iron rails, and wider (standard) gauge, together with cable-hauled or steam-operated wagons, or self-acting inclines (balanced, loaded wagons coming down, empty wagons going up) soon increased the tonnages five and ten times over.

By 1850 locomotives, track, wagons and ships had developed to the point where the Tyne itself was unable to handle the traffic. The opening of huge wooden staithes such as those at Dunston and South Shields made river training works essential.[3,4] From that date, the Tyne Improvement Commission took over responsibility for the river from Newcastle Corporation. Under its own Engineer, an extensive programme of dredging was undertaken by the Commission while the Consultant, James Walker, was retained to prepare designs for the two piers or training walls at the river mouth.

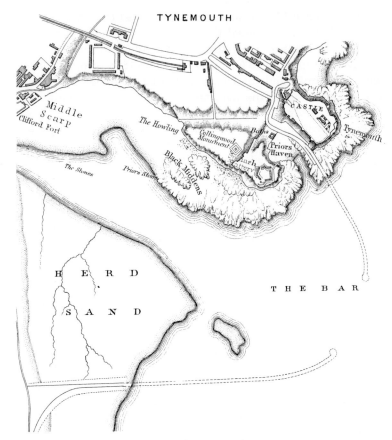

Figure 2/1. Tyne Piers

Walker's plans entailed the construction of a North Pier 700 yd long on the Tynemouth side and a South Pier 1400 yd long from South Shields. Construction began in 1855, the contractor being Benjamin Lawton, while P.J. Messent was appointed Resident Engineer. During construction, it was found necessary to increase the length of both piers, the North to 1020 yd and the South to 1712 yd, resulting in the foundations being laid in a much greater depth of water.

In 1862 Lawton's contract expired and all subsequent work was carried out by the Commission under the direction of Messent, who was responsible also for the design of the cranes used to place the masonry blocks weighing some 40 tons.[5] It was not until 1895 that work was completed, having been somewhat delayed by the extensive storm damage suffered by both piers during construction. The piers cost almost £2m to construct and involved the placing of some 3m tons of stone.

3. Ryhope Pumping Station   (HEW 180)   NZ 404 525

Although water had been supplied to the towns of Sunderland and South Shields very much earlier, it was in 1852 that the present Sunderland and South Shields Water Company was formed. As a result of a report submitted by Thomas Hawksley in 1860, pumping stations were constructed at Cleadon, Ryhope and Dalton, all these abstracting water from underground sources, unlike the neighbouring Newcastle and Gateshead Water Company which relied at that time on both impounding reservoirs and river pumping.

The pumping station at Ryhope, now in the care of the Ryhope Engines Trust, was constructed between 1865 and 1869, a feature of construction being the use of one of the engines to dewater the well during its sinking. The main well, 15 ft in diameter, was sunk to a depth of 253 ft, while the other, an ellipse, reached 140 ft.[6]

Above the well were placed two compound beam engines built in Newcastle by R. and W. Hawthorn, each engine having a pump stroke of 10 ft 8 in and with cylinders of 23½ in and 45 in diameter and a steam pressure of 30 lb/in^2, capable of pumping 40 000 gal/h. Steam was supplied to the engines from an adjacent boiler house containing six Cornish boilers which were replaced in 1908 by Lancashire boilers.

Built by William Jackson of Newcastle to Hawksley's design, the engine house, boiler house, 160 ft high chimney, cooling pond and reservoir are pleasingly decorative and form a distinctive example of the industrial architecture of the period, the Victorian Gothic style. The pumping station is operated on a regular basis, principally at Bank Holiday weekends, when the engines are steamed.

4. Newcastle–Carlisle Road   (HEW 517)   NZ 238 642 to NY 400 568

As a result of transport problems met in countering the 1745

Rebellion in Scotland, an Act of Parliament was obtained in 1751 for the construction of a new road between the towns of Newcastle and Carlisle, now known as the Military Road.[7]

For most of its length of 56 miles the road follows, and in places lies upon, Hadrian's Wall, which also formed a convenient quarry for construction materials. The width of construction was originally 27 ft between ditches and the actual carriageway was 16 ft wide; road formation was 15 in thick at the crown and 5 in at the edges. Bridges were 14 ft wide between parapets.

Although not literally a turnpike, tolls were extracted for use of the road and 14 toll houses were built, of which only two survive, the disappearance of so many being due to the constant road improvements which have been made over the years.

The line of the road was first surveyed by Dugal Campbell, Sub-Director of Engineers, and construction lasted from 1751 to 1757. For part of its length the surveyor in charge of the work was John Brown, brother of landscape gardener 'Capability', while the work was undertaken by several contractors.

5. Hexham Bridge, Northumberland   (HEW 535)
NY 941 647 and NY 929 652

On 17 November 1771 a disastrous flood on the Tyne destroyed all bridges on the river with the exception of the crossing at Corbridge (HEW 995). John Smeaton was asked to undertake the design of the new bridge at Hexham and it was begun in 1778, damaged during construction, completed in 1780 but collapsed in March 1782, only two arches remaining intact. Following reports from both Smeaton and Mylne the bridge was rebuilt to Smeaton's design[8] under the supervision of the County Bridge Surveyors, Robert Thompson and William Johnson.

This masonry bridge, similar to those at Coldstream and Perth, comprises nine arches with spans varying from 37 to 51 ft, the end ones being semi-elliptical and all others segmental; to simplify centering, all are formed to the same radius. The cutwaters are pointed with a 90° angle and are founded on extensive piling and framing. Each spandrel shows a circular ring of masonry with four keystones. During a major strengthening in 1965 the spandrels were filled with large diameter pipes while cantilevered reinforced concrete footways were formed, so increasing the width between parapets from 18 to 30 ft.

In Hexham also, the cast iron roof trusses of the railway station (HEW 924) are of some interest. Larger examples of this type of roof may be seen at Durham (HEW 453) and at Selby (HEW 518).

6. Roman Bridges, Chollerford   (HEW 761)   NY 914 701

The north of England is rich in evidence of the Roman occupation and, apart from Hadrian's Wall itself, the remains of two bridges at Chollerford are of great interest in that they form what is probably the earliest relic of civil engineering in the area.[9]

On the line of the Wall the remains of a bridge abutment and an earlier bridge pier can be seen on the east bank of the river North Tyne. The pier is part of an early bridge, thought probably to

Figure 2/2. Causey Arch

precede the Wall, and this bridge comprised piers 9 ft 4 in by 10 ft 4 in with spans of 41 ft 2 in. Following the construction of the bridge it would seem that the river changed its course, leading the second bridge to be constructed more than a century later with its eastern abutment incorporating the older first pier within it. The later bridge consisted of piers with parallel sides 21 ft 6 in in length and 16 ft wide, so leading to the conclusion that its deck was of much greater width than that of the earlier structure; spans were 35 ft 6 in.

7. Causey Arch, Tanfield   (HEW 89)   NZ 201 559
Figure 2/2

Reputedly the oldest 'railway' bridge in the world, the Causey Arch carried the Tanfield Waggonway over the Causey Burn, and was built in 1727 by Ralph Wood, mason. Claimed to be the fifth largest span masonry railway bridge in Britain, even today, it remained the largest stone span for 30 years, its nearest rival being the road bridge at Twizel, between Coldstream and Berwick. The arch is of semi-elliptical form, 35 ft high from springing to soffit with a span of 105 ft; its height is 80 ft and it would seem to have carried a double track. Such was its importance that the eminent architect, Nicholas Hawksmoor, wrote of it in 1736 as 'a bold Arch lately built near Newcastle for convenience of the Coal trade, which must be here mentioned for the largeness of its span'. It is now the property of the Durham County Council and has recently been repaired. [10]

8. Ouseburn Viaduct   (HEW 193)   NZ 263 647
Willington Viaduct   (HEW 194)   NZ 316 667
Figure 2/3

The Newcastle and North Shields Railway was completed in 1839, the Engineers responsible for the design of its bridges being John and Benjamin Green, of Newcastle. As architects and engineers the Greens were responsible for several bridges and buildings in the north east, but the two viaducts on this line were unusual in being of laminated timber arch construction to the Wiebeking system.

The Ouseburn Viaduct comprises five spans, each of 131 ft to centres, the arches themselves being of 116 ft span and 32 ft 6 in rise; the height of the track above foundation is 108 ft and the total length of the structure is 918 ft. The original viaduct was built by

Figure 2/3. (Above) Willington Viaduct; (below) Ouseburn Viaduct

Messrs J. Welch and the timber arches were replaced by iron in 1869, the contractors then being the Weardale Iron and Coal Company. The viaduct was widened to carry four tracks in 1885, the contractor in that year being Messrs Walter Scott.

The Willington Viaduct is similar in construction with seven spans of up to 128 ft; its height is 82 ft and it, too, was replaced by iron arches in 1869. The original contractors were Messrs Robson. The timber arches comprised 14 layers of timber, each 22 in by 3½ in, held by trenails.

These two viaducts are reputed to be the earliest laminated timber arch railways bridges in Britain, and it is of interest to note that the Greens proposed to span the river Tyne in a similar manner, but their proposals were not put into effect.[11] [12]

They are often quoted as outstanding examples of bridgework using timber as the structural material. It is perhaps not generally recognised now how important timber used to be in this context and this is partly because of questions of durability. Many of the

Figure 2/4. Victoria Viaduct

major viaducts in the early days of railway building had timber superstructures of various types. Brunel's fan viaducts are well remembered and the old Great Northern Railway used heavy framed trusses. Laminated arches were favoured by many engineers following the success of Ouseburn and Willington.

The adjacent road viaduct is a not inconsiderable structure, while the new Byker Viaduct, sited between the two older structures, for the new Tyne and Wear Metro system, has features of great interest to bridge engineers.

9. Victoria Viaduct, Penshaw   (HEW 156)
NZ 320 546   Figure 2/4

On 24 August 1838 Victoria Viaduct, the major work of the Durham Junction Railway, was completed, so providing a crossing of the river Wear.[13] The Viaduct between Ferryhill and Pelaw (part of the old main line from Darlington to Gateshead) comprises four main arches of 100, 160, 144 and 100 ft spans respectively, with six minor spans of 20 ft each. The total length of the bridge is 811 ft and the tracks are carried at a height of 120 ft above the river.

An iron bridge was first proposed by John Green, a Newcastle architect, but his design was rejected in favour of the masonry structure proposed by James Walker, a bridge based on the pattern of Trajan's Bridge at Alcantara in Spain where spans of 98 ft carry the roadway at a height of 170 ft. The three small spans at each end of the Victoria bridge did not form part of Walker's original design. The bridge was in fact constructed by John Gibb and Sons of Aberdeen, to the requirements of Thomas E. Harrison.

The 160 ft span masonry arch is only exceeded on British Railways by that at Ballochmyle.

10. Hownes Gill Viaduct   (HEW 157)   NZ 096 491
Figure 2/5

One of the most spectacular viaducts in north east England is that at Hownes Gill near Consett. The viaduct was completed in 1858 and was designed by Thomas Bouch.[14] The clients were the Stockton and Darlington Railway Company and the contractor John Anderson.

The viaduct is a very graceful structure, constructed of firebrick, and it reaches a height of 150 ft above the valley floor, its 730 ft length carrying a single track railway, now disused. Prior to the construction of the viaduct the railway company worked a double incline system to cross the valley, a method which became a severe bottleneck; hence its replacement.

Bouch's designs were submitted to Robert Stephenson for approval and his only recommendation was that inverted arches be used under the five central piers to reduce ground loading—the piers are recessed to reduce loadings still further.

11. Monkwearmouth Station   (HEW 290)   NZ 396 577

The north east is fortunate to possess two railway stations of excellent architectural design, Newcastle and Monkwearmouth. Designed originally as the terminus of the Brandling Junction Railway, serving trains from Newcastle and South Shields, the station at Monkwearmouth stands on the north bank of the river Wear and was converted for through running in 1876 with the erection of a bridge over the river.

Long attributed to John Dobson, the station was in fact designed by Thomas Moore, a Sunderland architect, and was opened in June 1848, at which time George Hudson was both Chairman of the York, Newcastle and Berwick Railway and MP for Sunderland.

The single-storey classical building comprises an Ionic two-storey portico at the centre with Doric end pavilions. It was purchased by Sunderland Corporation in 1971, since when it has been converted into a museum housing principally railway exhibits, and is well worth a visit.

12. Newcastle Central Station   (HEW 289)
NZ 246 638   Figure 2/6

Both the station buildings (HEW 289) and the station roof or 'train shed' (HEW 452) are extremely notable structures. They are the work of John Dobson, the well known local architect, who was awarded a medal at the 1858 Paris Exhibition for his roof design.[15] This is the first of many major railway station roofs having curved iron ribs of considerable span. It was brought into use as early as 1850; those at York and Darlington for instance date from 1877 and 1887 respectively; Paddington is more contemporary with Newcastle.

Newcastle Central Station lies roughly east–west, on a curve, and originally accommodated two separate railways, the Newcastle and

Figure 2/5. Hownes Gill Viaduct

Figure 2/6. Central Station, Newcastle (British Rail)

Carlisle from the west and the York, Newcastle and Berwick from the east. Both terminated in Central Station. Through working to Edinburgh was not instituted until 1862 and even then not fully until the King Edward VII Bridge was opened in 1906.

The south side of the station, nearest to the river, is a modern extension. The original roof comprises the three more northerly spans, adjoining the station buildings; these form a large and impressive piece of architecture, enhanced by a splendid portico added in 1861.

There are two lines of rather plain cast iron roof columns at 30 ft centres, with arcades of very simple arched girders about 5 ft deep at the columns, having completely open spandrels. The height is 23 ft 4 in to the top. The arched roof ribs are about 62 ft span and at 10 ft centres, and the centre span is set 6 ft 6 in higher than the other two. This is done by extending the cast iron columns upward and incorporating shoes for the ends of queen post timber and iron trusses which are boxed in and panelled.

The main roof ribs are simple (web plus four angle) plate girders 9½ in deep by 6 in wide, with 2¾ by 2¾ by ⅜ in angles and ⅜ in web. The contractors were Hawks Crawshay and Sons, of Gateshead.

13. Dean Street arch bridge, Newcastle upon Tyne   (HEW 334)   NZ 251 640

The former York, Newcastle and Berwick Railway, now the east coast main line, is carried over Newcastle's Dean Street by means of a magnificent semi-elliptical or five-centred masonry arch of 78 ft span and some 80 ft high from road to track. This arch was built in 1848 and the line was widened in 1894, the additional arch being of 106 ft span. The earlier arch was constructed by Benjamin Lawton in 1847 and the later one by Walter Scott and Company.

The main arch has 25 ft approach spans forming part of a viaduct 814 yd in length but it differs in detail from the remainder of the viaduct, so casting doubts as to the designer involved. It was possibly John Dobson.

14. No. 5 Bridge, Newcastle upon Tyne   (HEW 36)   NZ 250 638

Immediately to the east of the Central Station on the line to

Berwick-upon-Tweed is a cast iron segmental arch bridge carrying rail over road. The bridge has a span of 60 ft and a rise of 8 ft 1½ in. there are six H-section ribs and the spandrels are X-pattern, all cast by Abbot and Company of Gateshead. It was built in 1848 and widened in 1893 to the designs of C.A. Harrison, this time in wrought iron, the eight new ribs matching the old. Like the Dean Street arch the designer of the original bridge cannot be established with confidence.

15. High Level Bridge, Newcastle upon Tyne (HEW 22)   NZ 252 437   Figure 2/7

The most notable Historical Engineering Work in Newcastle is undoubtedly the High Level Bridge carrying the east coast main line railway across the River Tyne. It is a double deck bridge with the public road linking Gateshead with Newcastle on the lower level.

The Engineer for the bridge was Robert Stephenson, assisted by Thomas E. Harrison, and the first contract was let during July 1846. Comprising six main spans, each of 125 ft, the rails are carried at a height of 120 ft above the river; the masonry approach viaducts are each 251 ft in length.

Each main span consists of four cast iron arch ribs. The rail deck is supported at the level of the crowns by cast iron columns and the road deck is at the level of the springing, hung from the arches by wrought iron tension rods. The outward thrust of the main arches is counteracted by wrought iron tension chains at road deck level.

The contractors for the ironwork of the bridge were Hawks Crawshay and Sons while the castings were provided by various local companies. The river piers and the northern approaches were built by Rush and Lawton while the south approach was the responsibility of Wilson and Gibson. Nasmyth's steam hammer was used in driving the piles carrying the piers, one of the first civil engineering works in which it was employed. This bridge, with the Royal Border Bridge at Berwick, formed the last of the major links in the railway between London and Edinburgh and was officially opened by Queen Victoria on 28 September, 1849.

Many details of the structure are to be found in the very full report by Captain Laffan, Inspecting Officer of Railways, dated 11 August, 1849.[16]

16. King Edward VII Railway Bridge, Newcastle   (HEW 256)   NZ 247 633

During the 19th century northbound trains entered Newcastle Central Station from the east end via High Level Bridge. Through running of traffic on the east coast main line was not possible until a new bridge was built in 1906, about 800 yd upstream of the older bridge, and connecting to the west end of the Station.[17] Although it is overshadowed by its older and more famous neighbour, the King Edward Bridge is undoubtedly a very handsome structure.

It was designed by C.A. Harrison and comprises two main spans, each of 300 ft, carrying four tracks over the river Tyne. There are end spans of 191 and 231 ft respectively. The 'lattice' girders of the bridge are of the double Warren type 28 ft deep and carry the railway at a height of approximately 112 ft above river level. Founded on rock throughout, construction involved the sinking of caissons to a depth of up to 69 ft below high water. The granite piers above cutwater level are built as triple shafts.

The contractors were Cleveland Bridge and Engineering Co. Ltd of Darlington, and the girders were built up in situ on trestling.

The excellent view of the three major bridges downstream (the High Level, the Swing Bridge and the Tyne Arch) obtained when crossing this bridge is now limited (or enhanced according to taste) by the completion of yet another bridge in between, to carry the Tyne and Wear Metro.

Upstream is the Redheugh bridge. The 1901 version (HEW 925) is of technical interest in that Pennsylvania trusses were used for its four spans. This is an unusual form of N-truss girder. Its predecessor was also interesting and unusual being a double Warren cable-stayed cantilever bridge with cast iron tubular booms which also served as water and gas mains. It was built in 1870 to the designs of Thomas Bouch.

17. Newcastle Swing Bridge   (HEW 92)   NZ 253 637
Figure 2/7

The earliest crossings of the Tyne at Newcastle were at low level. The Romans built a bridge there and its 13th century replacement, destroyed by the floods of 1771, was followed by a masonry arch bridge designed by Robert Mylne and built between 1772 and 1779.

Such a bridge however prevented sizable ships from using the river upstream of it, and the establishment of an engineering works

Figure 2/7. High Level Bridge with Swing Bridge in foreground,
Newcastle (City of Newcastle upon Tyne City Engineer's Office)

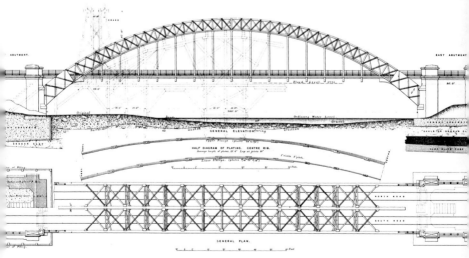

Figure 2/8. Wylam wrought iron bridge

at Elswick, west of Newcastle, by William George Armstrong, later to become Lord Armstrong and President of the Institution of Civil Engineers, led to consideration being given to its replacement by a movable bridge.

The River Tyne Improvement Commissioners were responsible for the new bridge which was completed in 1876, to the designs of John F. Ure. Appropriately it was built by Sir William Armstrong and Company.

It was described as the largest of its type in Great Britain and comprises a single swinging section 281 ft long providing two clear openings each 110 ft wide, flanked by fixed spans of 92 and 64 ft. The swinging section weighs 1200 tons and is opened hydraulically, the major part of the weight being taken by a central relieving press, the remainder by rollers. The foundations comprise cast iron cylinders sunk to a rock base.

The bridge, originally operated by steam pumps driving hydraulic engines, can swing through 180° in 3 minutes following a ship as it passes through the opening. Operation is now by means of electrically operated pumps although the original hydraulic system has been retained.

18. Tyne Bridge, Newcastle   (HEW 91)   NZ 254 638

The rapid growth of road traffic in the 20th century made another fixed high-level crossing essential and the Tyne Bridge was opened by King George V in 1928.

The bridge is a two-pin steel arch, and at the time of its construction was the longest of its type in Britain with a span between pins of 531 ft. The bridge was designed by Mott Hay and Anderson and comprises two main parabolic trusses with Warren bracing, each a maximum of 20 ft 3 in deep at mid-span, and these trusses carry the roadway at a height of 93 ft above the river, giving a clearance of 84 ft 6 in at high tide. The arches themselves rise to a height above the pins of 170 ft and carry a road deck 56 ft wide suspended from them.

The pins are backed by twin towers at each end of the bridge and the approach spans are carried on octagonal columns, these spans being variable up to a maximum of 154 ft. Built by Dorman Long and Co. Ltd, the main span of the bridge contains some 4000 tons of steel, 2400 in the arch itself, while a further 4000 tons is incorporated in the approaches.[18]

19. Wrought iron arch bridge, Wylam   (HEW 19)
NZ 111 643   Figure 2/8

Following the closure of the Wylam waggonway, with which George Stephenson was associated (his house may still be seen at Wylam) the Scotswood, Newburn and Wylam Railway was built to serve the north side of the Tyne, leaving the Newcastle and Carlisle Railway at Scotswood and joining it again at Wylam, immediately to the west of an arch bridge constructed to cross the river.

An early example of its type and perhaps ahead of its time, the bridge has three ribs spanning 240 ft and carried a double track. it was designed by W.G. Laws, later to become City Engineer of Newcastle, and was constructed in wrought iron by Hawks Crawshay and Sons of Gateshead in 1876. Its lattice ribs are 7 ft deep at the crown and 10 ft at the springing.[19] The railway was closed in 1968 but the bridge, now the property of the Local Authority, has been preserved as a pedestrian crossing of the river.

20. Wearmouth Bridge, Sunderland   (HEW 762)
NZ 396 574

The Wear also has its quota of big bridges. Wearmouth Bridge is a three-pin arch of 375 ft span completed in 1929. Built to replace an earlier structure without interrupting the road traffic crossing the river, it was designed by Mott Hay and Anderson and erected by Sir W. Arrol and Co. Ltd.[20] It replaced an earlier and more famous bridge on the site (HEW 528), the cast iron arch of 236 ft span credited to R. Burdon and cast by Walkers of Rotherham with two tiers of cast iron voussoirs. It was completed in 1796 and was reconstructed in 1858 under the supervision of Robert Stephenson.

21. Wear Bridge, Sunderland   (HEW 728)
NZ 396 574   Figure 2/9

The original Brandling Junction Railway from Newcastle terminated at Monkwearmouth. In 1876 the line, then part of the North Eastern Railway, was extended southwards into Sunderland, crossing the Wear by means of a hog-back Vierendeel girder bridge designed by T.E. Harrison.

The bridge has a clear span of 300 ft and the twin girders are 42 ft deep at their centres. Verticals in the bowstrings are placed at 20 ft centres and are stiffened at their junction by means of curved

Figure 2/9. Wear Bridge, Sunderland (D. Gordon Swinton)

bracings, imparting to the structure the effect of elliptical piercing through the girders. The clearance above the river is 86 ft and the bridge incorporates three masonry arches of 25 ft span at each end. The contractor was John Waddell.

There is yet another major bridge over the River Wear at the west side of Sunderland. This had the distinction of being the heaviest single span in Great Britain when built in 1909. The Queen Alexandra Bridge, like the High Level Bridge in Newcastle is a double-deck rail/road bridge but only the lower deck for road traffic is still in use.

22. Reinforced concrete warehouse, Newcastle (HEW 979)   NZ 255 640

Because L.G. Mouchel established an office in Newcastle, the north east of England boasts several early reinforced concrete structures, built on the principles evolved by Hennebique. Several such structures were commissioned by the Co-operative Wholesale Society and a warehouse, completed in 1901, is still in use on the quayside in Newcastle upon Tyne.

The building was constructed by Brims and Co., a Newcastle firm of contractors, and is completely of reinforced concrete. The plan area is 124 ft by 90 ft with columns at approximately 15 ft centres; the building is eight storeys high. Built on a raft foundation the structure includes columns which vary in size from 29 in square at basement level to 8 in square at the upper floor. Floor beams are 8 in by 12 in deep and floor slabs 7 in thick, being designed to carry 6 cwt/ft^2.

A 30 ft span vaulted arch roof 3 in thick was added in 1909.

CHAPTER 3

County Durham
and Cleveland

At the time of the construction of the Stockton and Darlington Railway in 1825 the principal ports on the river Tees were Stockton and Yarm. Before the railway was built, a canal had been under consideration but the development of waggonways was very

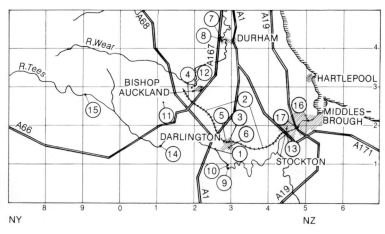

1. Darlington Pumping Station
2. Stockton and Darlington Railway
3. Skerne Bridge, Darlington
4. Gaunless Bridge substructure, West Auckland
5. Darlington North Road Station
6. Darlington Bank Top train shed roof
7. Durham Station roof
8. Durham Viaduct
9. Croft Viaduct
10. Croft Bridge
11. Skew arch bridge, Haggerleazes
12. No. 12 Bridge, Bishop Auckland
13. Tees Suspension Bridge, Stockton
14. Whorlton Bridge
15. Wynch Bridge
16. Middlesbrough Transporter Bridge
17. Newport Lift Bridge

advanced in the north east, particularly serving the Tyne and Wear. The production of a satisfactory wrought iron rail coincided with the engineering ability of George Stephenson in the locomotive field. This was brought to the notice of the wealthy Pease family and led eventually to the construction of the railway, a new kind of railway in which distance and speed could be exploited. It was this railway too which, by its extension to Middlesbrough in 1830, was to be responsible for the rapid growth of that town, the population soon overtaking that of others in the region.

Development was aided also by the discovery, in the mid-19th century, of ironstone in the Cleveland area, this in turn leading to the establishment of ironworks, while the exploitation of brine wells at Billingham was the precursor of the vast complex of chemical works soon to be built.

Coal was first exported from the north east through the rivers Tyne and Wear, but the mining of the deeper seams in the eastern parts of County Durham led to the establishment of new outlets, the ports of Middlesbrough, Hartlepool and Seaham, the last being built privately by Lord Londonderry in 1831 (see Chapter 2). With the ports came an extension and proliferation of railways necessary both for exporting coal and also for the transport of iron ore and limestone; most were amalgamated into the North Eastern Railway in 1854, but it was not until 1863 that the Stockton and Darlington system lost its identity.

Although the river Tees was crossed by several early bridges, including a fine suspension bridge at Whorlton, the necessity of providing better communication within the town limits of Middlesbrough led to the construction in 1911 of the Transporter Bridge, replacing a ferry, and in 1934 to the Newport Lift Bridge, both structures designed so as not to impede river traffic.

1. Darlington Pumping Station   (HEW 534)   NZ 258 139

The Darlington Gas and Water Company was formed by the Pease family in 1849 and some five years later the works were taken over by what was to become the Darlington Corporation Water Department and the Stockton, Middlesbrough and Yarm Water Company, later the Tees Valley and Cleveland Water Board.

A pumping station had been built at Darlington in 1849 to abstract water from the river Tees, and in 1903 these works were extended by the Corporation and a further pumping station built, this one to house a beam engine, designed by T. and C. Hawksley, and built by Teesdale Brothers of Darlington; it is believed to be the last installation of its kind in Britain.

The engine works at a steam pressure of 100 lb/in², the cylinders of 18 and 29 in diameter and strokes of 5 ft 3 in and 7 ft being of such capacity as to produce 140 h.p. The pumps are capable of raising 1800 gal/min to a head of 125 ft. A similar set of pumps is powered by a Hornsby gas engine of 220 h.p. which was installed in 1913.

The station is not normally open to the public and is now in the ownership of the Northumbrian Water Authority.

2. Stockton and Darlington Railway   (HEW 85)
NZ 167 294 to NZ 449 183   Figure 3/1

Vehicles of a sort, generally small and operated singly, have run on rails of a kind, usually wooden and set to a variety of gauges, since the 16th century. Motive power was man, the horse or gravity and speeds much above walking pace were not possible. Distances were short so statutory powers were seldom, if ever, necessary to establish the route. Passengers were not catered for. These were waggonways or tramroads rather than the transport system we now know as railways, even in their early form of 150 years ago.

Many such systems have been claimed to be the 'first' railway but enquiry reveals that it was only in respect of one or two of the above factors. The Stockton and Darlington Railway is generally accepted to be the first to incorporate all of them. The very length and scale of it, from Shildon to Stockton via Darlington and its subsequent development are sufficient to overcome the rather shaky claim to have had the first locomotive hauled passenger service. This operated on the opening day, but then reverted to horse drawn coaches for the next eight years, the available locomotives being reserved for freight.

It was the first major work by George Stephenson and was intended to carry minerals from Witton Park and district, near Shildon, for shipment on the Tees at Stockton. Following proposals for the construction of a canal, an Act for the railway was finally passed in 1821 and the line opened in September 1825. It was initially worked eastwards from Shildon using both locomotives and horses for motive power. At the western end stationary engines were installed at the Brusselton and Etherley

Figure 3/1. Opening of Stockton and Darlington Railway,
September 27 1825, by John Dobbin; Skerne Bridge is on the right
(Borough of Darlington Museum).

inclines. Railway branches were added later at Black Boy and
Haggerleazes, and in 1830 the system was extended across the
river to Middlesbrough by means of a suspension bridge designed
by Captain Samuel Brown RN and described later (HEW 717).

The permanent way comprised a mixture of cast iron and
malleable iron fish-bellied rails supported on stone sleepers, and
the track, at first only a single line, was duplicated in 1831. Several
of the original works may still be seen, and while parts of the line
are still in use by British Rail, others have been abandoned and reopened as footpaths.[1] The frequently illustrated Skerne bridge, and
the skew arch bridge at Haggerleazes have survived at site, as has
the substructure of Stephenson's bridge over the river Gaunless at
West Auckland.

3. Skerne Bridge, Darlington   (HEW 151)   NZ 292 156
This bridge features in the well known painting by Dobbin of the
opening of the railway in 1825. Although now somewhat
disfigured by alterations and screened by a gasworks, the bridge is
still in use. It comprises a central masonry segmental arch of 39 ft 6
in span with flanking round-headed arches of 8 ft span separated
from it by 8 ft wide piers.

The original structure of the bridge is 22 ft wide but corbelling gives a greater outside width at parapet level, some 40 ft above the river. Although George Stephenson was Engineer to the Railway, the bridge was designed by Ignatius Bonomi, a Durham architect, and built by Francis Peacock of Yarm.

4. Gaunless Bridge Substructure, West Auckland   (HEW 190)   NZ 186 266

Unlike Skerne Bridge, the site of Gaunless Bridge is still rural, although partly enclosed by housing estates through which access is easily obtainable. The iron superstructure of the bridge is now at York (see Chapter 4) at the National Railway Museum, but the substructure still on site is a very attractive piece of masonry. It is simple and functional with just sufficient enhancement by moulded details to stamp it with the hallmark of quality.

5. North Road Station, Darlington   (HEW 288)   NZ 289 157   Figure 3/2

North Road Station was not the first one serving the town. It was originally built by the Stockton and Darlington Railway in 1842, since which time it has been altered several times. As standing, the station comprises a single-storey range of offices some 400 ft in

Figure 3/2. North Road Station, Darlington (North Road Station Museum)

length with an external two-storey feature, supported by seven cast iron columns, forming a central portico. Behind this is the train shed which comprises timber trusses of 55 ft span. Extended in 1873, it has been reduced to its original size since its conversion to museum use on 27 September, 1975.

It features a particularly attractive cast iron spiral staircase and houses various exhibits including the two locomotives, *Locomotion No. 1* and *Derwent*, so long a feature of the present main line station (Bank Top).

6. Darlington Bank Top Train Shed Roof   (HEW 439)
NZ 294 141

The improving quality and available sizes of plates and sections in wrought iron in the 1840s led not only to rivetted plate girders, box girders and tubular bridges but to large arched ribs for train shed roofs and other buildings. Newcastle (1849) and Paddington (1850) were followed by many others including York (1877) and Darlington (1887).

Cast iron plates with heraldic devices used as facings to the structural member were very popular in this period and the arms of the North Eastern Railway and of the places served add interest to this roof at Bank Top.

The station is basically an island platform with a down (northbound) and up face, served by a central subway from the down side and a vehicular ramp at the north end. There are station buildings down the island spine and bay lines at each end. The overall roof is more than 1000 ft long with three spans of wrought iron arched ribs varying from 62 to 66 ft span at 19 to 27 ft centres on cast iron columns and arcades—in all 47 bays. There are lattice purlins at 4 ft 7 in centres covered by boarding and slates in the lower parts of the arch and by roof glazing above. James Thomson was the contractor.

7. Durham Station Roof   (HEW 453)   NZ 270 428

Although it was constructed in 1857, the station at Durham did not then form part of the east coast main line. It became so in 1870, at which time a new roof was added, very unusual in form. A similar roof was later built at Selby (HEW 518) and there is a small one at Hexham (HEW 924). Although part of this roof at Durham has now been removed, the down platform section of it remains.

Comprising cast iron Vierendeel-type trusses with a span between columns of 34 ft 6 in and end cantilevers of 9 ft 10½ in and 9 ft 6 in, the roof is supported by 8 ft high columns surmounted by spandrel supports 3 ft 6 in deep, so giving a clearance above the platform of 11 ft 6 in. The trusses are 5 ft deep and spaced at 15 ft centres over 14 bays and are extended at the south end of the platform by a further six bays spanning ony 14 ft 6 in. It was built while Thomas Prosser was architect to the North Eastern Railway.

8. Durham Viaduct   (HEW 226)   NZ 269 426
The viaduct which carries the east coast main line through Durham city was built as part of the Bishop Auckland branch of the North Eastern Railway in 1854. It comprises eleven arches of 60 ft span and is 76 ft high. Although the original plans show 3 ft 4 in span semi-circular corbelled arches as a decorative support to stone parapets, similar to those of the Royal Border Bridge, the present arrangement is an iron parapet fence fixed to cast iron cantilever brackets which were added in 1895.

The structure is of masonry facing with brick soffits to the arches and is built on a curve. The contractor was Richard Cail, responsible for several works on Tyneside. From this viaduct and station there are magnificent views of Durham Cathedral and Castle.

9. Croft Viaduct   (HEW 572)   NZ 291 091
The railway viaduct at Croft, carrying the east coast main line over the river Tees, was opened for passenger traffic in March 1841. Originally forming part of the Great North of England Railway it was designed by Henry Welch and constructed by Deas and Hogg over a period of seven years.

With a total length of 471 ft and a height, from river to arch soffit, of some 50 ft, the four arches span 45 ft square, or 59 ft on a skew of 49° 31'. The fine quality of the masonry with its panelled pier ends is typical of this period of railway construction.

10. Croft Bridge   (HEW 208)   NZ 290 098   Figure 3/3
The railway crosses the A167 just south of the Tees and the road itself crosses the river on the North Yorks–Durham county boundary about half a mile to the north. This bridge is a scheduled Ancient Monument and one of the larger and more massive of

Figure 3/3. Croft Bridge (National Monuments Record)

Figure 3/4. Tees Suspension Bridge

early road bridges. It is 330 ft long with seven pointed arches, five of them of 37 ft span, two of them smaller. Six arches have narrow ribs. There is a 24 ft carriageway and two footways. It was probably built in the 15th century and was widened in 1795.

11. Skew arch bridge, Haggerleazes   (HEW 514)
NZ 117 256

The history of the skew arch is obscure but one of the earliest records of its use in the British Isles is that by William Chapman, who in his later years designed Seaham Harbour (HEW 758). He used it during the construction of the Kildare Canal in Ireland in about 1787 and it later came to be widely employed on canal and railway works. There were two on the Rochdale Canal and an early example of its use in conjunction with railways is the bridge near the western end of the Haggerleazes branch of the Stockton and Darlington Railway. Another example is the more famous bridge on the Liverpool and Manchester Railway at Rainhill (HEW 553) (Chapter 8).

The bridge at Haggerleazes carries the railway over the river Gaunless and consists of a single masonry segmental skew arch,· the angle between the face of the bridge and face of the abutment being only 27°. On the face of the bridge, its span is 42 ft but its skew reduces this to a true 19 ft, the rise being 7 ft. With a total length of some 85 ft the width of the bridge between parapets is 12 ft.

Although the drawings of the railway line were prepared by Robert Stephenson, the design of the bridge is attributed to Thomas Storey.[2] The piling and foundations were constructed by Thomas Worth and John Batey; the arch and parapets were built by James Wilson of Pontefract in 1830. The parallel arch ring and hood mould present a neat, simple and attractive appearance.

12. No. 12 Bridge, Bishop Auckland   (HEW 307)
NZ 191 297

Girders having curved top and bottom flanges resemble a lens in shape and are rather rare. The famous 'Fish' bridge 1½ miles west of Devizes in Wiltshire had solid web plate girders and was built in 1857. It was.replaced in 1901 by a conventional truss bridge of 110 ft skew, 35 ft square span.

Robert Stephenson also designed and presumably built a solid web lenticular girder bridge at 64 ft skew (28°) span in 1835 to carry the Banbury to Lutterworth road over the London and Birmingham Railway; it was of cast iron with wrought iron ties.

Lenticular girders however usually have open webs; that is, they are composed of separate struts and ties forming a truss. By itself the hogbacked top member would be an arch and in compression, while the fish-bellied lower member alone would be in tension; together as a lenticular truss they form a stable unit.

The Royal Albert Bridge at Saltash (HEW 29) has this form; so has the Gaunless Bridge (HEW 190) and there is a multi-span example at Roxburgh (HEW 402, Chapter 1). No. 12 Bridge, carrying a farm road over the former Bishop Auckland and Weardale Railway, is intermediate in size having a clear skew span of 86 ft 3 in with the two trusses spaced at 11 ft centres. It has a timber deck on timber cross joists at 2 ft 4 in centres; every 14 ft the cross joist is of iron. The main top member is H-section cast iron and the bottom one is wrought iron flat link chain. There are 12 panels incorporating 11 verticals of round bar with diagonal flats alternately rising and falling. There is a lower bottom member of square bar coupled to the chain by cast clamps which carry the cross tie rods and there are horizontal and vertical cross bracings of wrought iron flat. The bridge was built in 1842 by the Shildon Works Company in conjunction with John Storey of Darlington.

13. Tees Suspension Bridge, Stockton   (HEW 717)
NZ 447 179   Figure 3/4

Few bridges have been so significant, sociologically and technically, as the suspension bridge built in 1830 to extend eastwards the Stockton and Darlington Railway. It presaged the expansion of the town of Middlesbrough, then a community of only some 40 inhabitants; technically it proved the impracticability of medium span suspension bridges for rail traffic.

It was 412 ft long with a main span of 281 ft. The deck, 16 ft wide, was suspended from 12 chains and gave a clearance above river level of 20 ft. The bridge was designed by Samuel Brown, who was at that time the leading exponent in Britain of this form of construction, but for road traffic (see Chapter 1). In spite of Brown's expertise this bridge proved quite incapable of carrying locomotives without unacceptable movement. On test with an 18 ton load the measured deflection of the bridge proved to be 9¼ in and later a load of 66 tons damaged the towers. It had to be replaced by a multi-span girder bridge whose successor of 1907 still marks the site.

14. Whorlton Bridge   (HEW 356)   NZ 106 145

On 13 October 1829 a bridge under construction on the river Tees was destroyed by a flood. At that time the old Scotswood suspension bridge over the Tyne was being built to the designs of John Green of Newcastle and it was this type of bridge which was chosen for Whorlton.

Begun in August 1830, the bridge spans 198 ft and the suspension chains comprise links made up from flat wrought iron bars 9 ft 10 in long, 3 in deep and 1 in wide. It has wrought iron cross bracing and a timber deck and was opened in July 1831. It was damaged by gales in 1976 and is now subjected to a weight restriction of three tons.

15. Wynch Bridge   (HEW 814)   NY 904 279

The river Tees is credited with the first suspension bridge in England, built to cross it some two miles upstream of Middleton. Erected in 1741, the Wynch Bridge (as it was then called) had a single span of about 70 ft with a width of 2 ft. It was a spidery affair not unlike a hammock, with no proper deck, and was used principally by local miners. It survived for 60 years until it collapsed in 1802, when it was replaced by a suspension bridge of more sturdy design. This was itself replaced by the present bridge early in the 20th century, some of the old chains being retained in a local museum.

16. Middlesbrough Transporter Bridge   (HEW 10)

NZ 501 213   Figure 3/5

From a population of 154 in 1831, Middlesbrough grew to 91 302 by 1901 and to improve communications to the north, an Act of Parliament was obtained in 1907 to permit the construction of a bridge, conditional upon river navigation not being affected.

The problem was overcome by adopting a transporter design[3] in which a travelling car, tested to a load of 80 tons, suspended by wires from a carriage, carries up to 600 persons or an equivalent load of vehicles across the river in some 2½ minutes. The carriage is supported by a steel truss having a span of 564 ft 9 in between

Figure 3/5. Middlesbrough Transporter Bridge (Dept of Planning, Cleveland County Council)

Figure 3/6. Newport Lift Bridge (Dept of Planning, Cleveland County Council)

the main towers and giving 160 ft clearance above high water. Cantilever end spans each 140 ft long balance the main span and are anchored to the ground by steel cables.

The bridge which was designed by Cleveland Bridge and Engineering Ltd and constructed by that company and Sir W. Arrol and Company Ltd was opened by Prince Arthur of Connaught in October 1911. There were similar bridges at Runcorn, Warrington and Newport, Gwent, although the first of these has been demolished.

17. Newport Lift Bridge   (HEW 470)   NZ 478 199
Figure 3/6

Middlesbrough boasts two bridges of unusual design; in addition to the transporter bridge a vertical lift bridge, crossing the river Tees at Newport, was opened in 1934, having been designed by Mott Hay and Anderson and built by Dorman Long.[4]

In order to safeguard the movement of shipping the bridge was designed to lift vertically over its centre span, the clearance of 21 ft in the lowered position being increased to 120 ft when raised; the navigation span so formed measures 260 ft. The lifting operation is by means of ropes passing through sheaves at the four corner towers, each rising to a height of 182 ft, and the lifting or lowering operation is completed in approximately 1½ minutes. Operation is by means of two 325 h.p. motors and the weight of steel in the lifting span is 1530 tons.

The bridge structure is carried on cast iron cylinders filled with concrete and sunk to a depth of 86 ft below high water level; the total weight of concrete used in the structure is 28 000 tons, while the weight of steel in the bridge and its approach spans is 8000 tons.

CHAPTER 4

York and North Yorkshire

THE Romans dominated these islands for 300 years. Their strength lay not only in their military achievement but also in their ability to organise public works on an immense scale. The quality and the simplicity of their building has allowed much of it to survive for the better part of 2000 years.

The Roman invasion commenced in the south east corner of England, in Kent, and they advanced west, north west, and north, building radial and peripheral roads in support. In AD 71–2 they moved northward from Lincoln, forded the Humber at Brough and set up a new headquarters at York, at the confluence of the Ouse and the Foss. The size of vessel in those days also permitted direct access from the sea at Spurn as well as from the Trent and its tributaries.

From York, Dere Street was built to run directly to Edinburgh. Parts of it later became the Great North Road (the A1) although the later trade routes tended to be diverted further east. Compared with the natural or lightly built trackways that preceded them, or the very sketchy attempts at road construction that followed and persisted until the days of Telford and Macadam, Roman ideas on building roads were remarkably complex and thorough.

The remains of one (HEW 824) can be seen at SE 810 985 on Wheeldale Moor, near Goathland. It led from Pickering to a signal station at Kettleness near Runswick Bay, a few miles west of Whitby. [1]

Water supply and drainage were other forms of public works which the Romans thought necessary. An interesting example (HEW 218), unearthed in York in 1972, is a length of sewer, with branches, still in working order, at SE 604 517 below Church Street. It is 150 ft long, 4 ft high and 2 to 3 ft wide, built partly of millstone grit and partly of large sandstone blocks. It has been fully explored, surveyed and recorded by the York Archaeological Trust.[2-4]

Moving on some 1500 years, a different need for water supply produced what is probably the earliest surviving railway locomotive water tank house. HEW 907 is in the old York and North Midland Railway yard at SE 595 515 behind the York

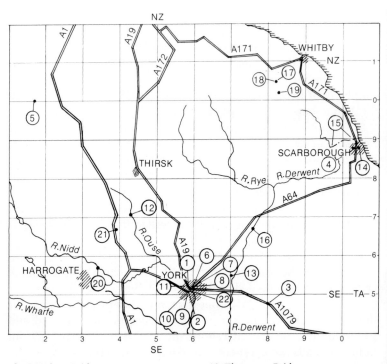

1. Gaunless Bridge
2. York Old Station
3. Pocklington Station roof
4. Scarborough Station roof
5. Richmond Station
6. York Minster, strengthening of central tower
7. York Minster, Chapter House roof
8. Bootham Bar, York
9. York (1877) Station roof
10. Lendal Bridge, York
11. York Waterworks, Acomb Landing
12. Thornton Bridge
13. Stamford Bridge Viaduct
14. Spa Bridge, Scarborough
15. Sea Cut, Scalby
16. Suspension footbridge, Huttons Ambo
17. Suspension footbridge, Grosmont
18. Grosmont (Horse) Tunnel
19. 'Scales' Bridge, Goathland
20. Knaresborough Viaduct
21. Cast iron bridge over Milby Cut
22. York City Bond

Railway Institute in Queen Street. It consists of a red brick building about 30 ft by 20 ft carrying a single tier of ten by six cast iron tank plates bearing the legends 'Y & N M' and 'John Walker York 1839'. This same firm of Walker cast the very fine railings which surround the British Museum in London.

Another link between York and London is the very popular

Figure 4/1. Roman Sewer, York (York Archaeological Trust)

National Railway Museum, which is not railway owned but a part of the Science Museum in the Department of Education and Science. Locomotives and coaches naturally predominate, but there are many other interesting exhibits. The one reason why railways have ever existed at all—the track—gets rather slight treatment, but this is recognised, and will doubtless be remedied one day. The broader aspects of civil engineering such as earthworks, bridges, tunnels and large buildings fare little better, perhaps because such works are common to other forms of transport or because it is difficult to present them adequately in a museum. Nevertheless some are presented in picture or model form, and there is one precious relic, outside the Museum but visible from within, namely the Gaunless Bridge.

1. Gaunless Bridge   (HEW 190)   now at SE 593 520
Figure 4/2
This fascinating little structure is a fragment of the original Stockton and Darlington Railway opened on 27 October 1825. It was located in the portion north west of Darlington and west of Shildon which was worked by stationary engines or by horses, isolated, in fact, between the Etherley and the Brusselton Inclines.

When locomotive working was extended westward to Bishop Auckland in 1842, the Gaunless bridge was first by-passed and later regirdered (c. 1901). The superstructure, that is to say the ironwork, was fortunately preserved, and some of it featured in the local Stockton and Darlington Railway centenary celebrations in 1925. Eventually, with the formation of a new Railway Museum at Queen Street, York, it was re-erected there between 1923 and 1929. When that museum was absorbed by the National Railway Museum, the bridge was dismantled, repaired and re-erected under the author's direction in 1975.

Although it was then 150 years old and had been assembled at least five times, it was only in service for quite a short period. It consists of four 12 ft 5 in spans of lenticular trusses on cast iron trestles, with a timber deck. The curved members are of wrought iron secured by casting into moulded vertical legs which continue upward to support the deck. The whole structure in elevation is not unlike a Victorian bedstead end and the method of fixing is similar, namely by interlocking not by bolting. The walkways are supported from the trestles on small cantilever brackets which also lock the main elements into position.

The design is attributed to George Stephenson in conjunction with John and Isaac Burrell, who ran the foundry in Newcastle where it was made.

The substructure of Gaunless Bridge is still in situ at West Auckland (see Chapter 3) and worth a visit if only for the quality of its masonry.

2. York Old Station   (HEW 13)   SE 598 517

York city walls are 500 years old and rise white and clean above their grassy ramparts, which, in the spring, are carpeted with daffodils. The length between Micklegate Bar and Lendal Bridge holds the railway at bay, as the present station is just outside them.

British Rail Eastern Region Headquarters Offices stand just within the walls, opposite, together with what remains of the old station which was a terminus and very limited in size. There are three points of interest about the Old Station, the first being that for the tracks to reach it the mediaeval walls had to be breached.

There are two large pointed arches near the corner of Queen Street. The one further from the York Railway Institute was in fact Bridge No. 51 carrying a footpath (the walls) over the York and North Midland Railway. It has a span of 66 ft 3 in and a width of 6 ft 4 in and is four centred. Thomas Cabrey, one of the George Stephenson team, was the York and North Midland Railway Engineer and produced a design for this arch, but the alternative scheme of a local architect, G.T. Andrews, was preferred.

Andrews subsequently built the second arch to serve the station yard, and another one near Lendal Bridge leading to the Great North of England Railway coal staithes on the River Ouse.

The design of important railway stations was not very far advanced in 1840 and there were several features about York which are notable. Some are due to Andrews, some to Cabrey, some perhaps to Thomas Storey, Engineer to the Great North of England Railway (for this was a joint station), and some no doubt to the influence of the Stephensons and of George Hudson.

The second feature of note is Andrews' range of offices serving both the station on its departure side, and the railway administration. They are still there and in use, facing Toft Green, simple but attractive, and surrounded by some of John or W. Tomlinson Walker's gates and railings.

The third feature is the old station roof or train shed of cast iron columns, arched cast iron girders, and wrought iron trusses in three bays. These bore a strong resemblance to old Euston (the terminus of the London and Birmingham Railway of 1835) which is not surprising, as, for a while, Euston to York was the main railway route to the north. Cabrey in fact visited other stations already built before producing a design for York. A small portion of the York train shed does remain but is not normally visible to the public.

3. Pocklington Station roof   (HEW 912)   SE 802 487

Several station roofs of similar pattern and age to York, however, can still be seen in the area. Perhaps the most interesting is Pocklington on the branch from York to Market Weighton, opened in 1847. This line was a pawn in the game of railway chess being played by George Hudson against rival promoters, and eventually formed part of the direct route between York and Hull, now closed. This particular country station with its buildings by G.T. Andrews and its overall roof or train shed has been absorbed by Pocklington School and converted into a gymnasium. As such it probably has the best chance of survival of any of these roofs. Malton and Filey are others, and there is a larger one at Scarborough.

4. Scarborough Station roof   (HEW 454)   TA 039 883

The branch line from York to Scarborough was authorised in 1844 and opened a year later. Over the years Scarborough station was extended again and again but since the end of the steam era has been pruned considerably. It is significant that almost the only roofs deemed worthy of retention are the original ones of 1845.

No doubt in a salt-laden atmosphere the use of wrought iron rather than steel is partly responsible for that, but for a standard span of about 40 ft the scantlings are extraordinarily light. The trusses are of the king post type at about 6 ft centres with 3 in by 2 in T principal rafters, five vertical rods, three 2 in by 2 in T struts each side and two main tie rods rising slightly to the centre post. The covering is diagonal boarding and slates on 1½ in by 1½ in angle purlins at 12 in centres.

Figure 4/2. Gaunless Bridge (York Railway Museum)

Figure 4/3. York Minster, strengthening of Tower (Shepherd Building Group)

5. Richmond Station   (HEW 618)   NZ 177 008

This is a slightly later and rather different version of railway station and train shed. There are two 30 ft spans, each of nine bays. The trusses have only three vertical members and the cast iron arcades between the eight cast iron columns are Gothic style with ornate spandrels. There are fewer and larger purlins but diagonal roof boarding is still employed. The station buildings designed by G.T. Andrews are well known in railway architecture and the ironwork was by John Walker of York. The branch line was closed in 1969 and the station buildings taken over by the Council and converted to other use.

6. York Minster, strengthening of Central Tower   (HEW 14)
SE 603 522   Figure 4/3

York Minster is a large building, dominating the skyline of York, and can be seen from many miles away. Views of the twin West Towers from Lendal Bridge or from the mediaeval walls are perhaps the best known, but structurally the huge Central Tower is the real problem. A good impression of the size of it can be obtained from Fishergate and the Selby Road.

This tower is 15th century work, and the third one on the site, which is also intersected by the remains of Roman building work. It is approximately 60 ft square and 180 ft high, and is supported on four complex pillars each taking more than 4000 tons load. It is almost central in the 500 ft length of the Minster, and its great weight has induced differential settlements of up to 1 ft. In the late 1960s it became clear that not only were the resulting stresses in the tower and adjacent masonry becoming too great, but that the tower foundations were in real trouble.

The story is told in detail by Dowrick and Beckmann[5] and the work in all took six years to complete. Briefly, however, the tower walls at various levels were drilled and stainless steel tie rods inserted. The four pier footings were expanded by an ingenious system of underpinning, preceded by an elaborate archaeological 'dig', with complex shoring, and a temporary backfill of sandbags, as the spoil was removed by narrow gauge railway (with human motive power!). Each pier was then surrounded at its base by a concrete mat 2 ft thick, on which a system of Freyssi flat jacks was laid. Next came a reinforced concrete collar 7 ft thick around the main pier base, and extending its area considerably. Ducts were fixed in the new concrete, and continued through the old masonry by drilling, and the whole then stressed by hydraulic jacks and stainless steel rods. An upper concrete collar 6 ft thick was added to stiffen the old stone footings, and pressure was then applied to the flat jacks and held for weeks and months until it was felt that a static position had been reached.

Cathedrals have been underpinned before (notably Winchester, HEW 182) but modern equipment and methods not only permitted a more ambitious scheme here, but are displayed permanently in the Undercroft, a new basement to the Minster. Instead of replacing all the old filling, the ground floor paving was relaid on a new reinforced concrete support, with coffered ceiling, and this new 'basement' is open to the public, and has a variety of uses.

Timber piles and rafts were widely used in the past for bridges and heavy building. The Central Tower had a raft consisting of two crossed rows of heavy oak baulks 12 in square and more. Similar baulks were used for its roof, and these have now been replaced by metal roof trusses.

The remainder of the Minster was underpinned later, the East Window posing a particular problem. The Architect (Surveyor to the Fabric) was Bernard Feilden, the Engineers were Ove Arup, the contractors Shepherds & Co. of York, and several noted archaeologists, associated with the Royal Commission on Historical Monuments, played an invaluable part in the project.

7. York Minster, Chapter House roof   (HEW 748)
SE 603 522

Adjacent to the Central Tower is the Chapter House, an octagonal building 63 ft across, and 66 ft 6 in high, with large external buttresses at the corners. It is quite separate from the main Minster building, and notable for its unrestricted floor space. There is no centre pillar, but instead a high pitched timber roof, of which a model is displayed. It dates from 1307.

8. Bootham Bar, York   (HEW 555)   SE 601 522

The mediaeval Bars (Gates) and walls of York are not without their maintenance problems. All four major Bars, Micklegate, Bootham, Monk, and Walmgate, are in daily use passing a large volume of road traffic into and out of the City. Three are relieved by side arches added in modern times, but traffic is much heavier at these than at Bootham, which is near the Minster, and has no side arches.

Bootham Bar dates from the 14th century and is 25 ft wide, 35 ft long and 46 ft high, a rectangular gatehouse with two upper storeys built of stone with timber floors, roof and portcullis. Its weight of 1000 tons is taken mostly on its two side walls. In 1951 it was found to be tilting to the south west and some restoration work was done.

In 1969 more positive measures were undertaken when over a hundred 5 in diameter Pali Radici piles were installed and steel tie bars inserted in cored holes horizontally at each upper floor level.

9. York (1877) Station roof   (HEW 239)   SE 596 517
Figure 4/4

On 31 July 1854 the York and North Midland Railway amalgamated with the Leeds Northern and the York, Newcastle and Berwick, to form the North Eastern Railway. Twenty years later, work began on a magnificent new station at York which would not only give vastly increased accommodation but also permit through running. It was completed and opened on 25 June 1877.

There are three main structures, the train shed itself, the station buildings and offices and the hotel. It is the former which is now described.

Built on a sharp curve, it has four spans of varying dimensions on three rows of cast iron columns between brick side walls. The main span over platforms 8 and 9 and two centre through lines on a 17 chain radius is 81 ft and the others are 45 ft, 55 ft and 57 ft 6 in. The length varies between 750 and 850 ft.

The cast iron columns have 27 in octagonal bases and circular shafts tapered from 21 in to 18 in diameter and there are nearly 100 of them in six different sizes; the tops have attractive decorations of acanthus leaves. They are spaced at between 30 and 31 ft centres on platform 8 and 28 to 29 ft centres on platform 9 and carry wrought iron girders with arched soffits, 2 ft deep at the column tops. To these girders are fixed cast iron heraldic panels, and above them are cast iron fretted panels and wrought iron horizontally bowed girders between the roof principals.

The wrought iron arch ribs are fixed-ended plate girders with a rise of about one third span and a depth at the crown of 14–18 in. The webs are pierced for decorative effect by stars, circles and quatrefoils. These ribs are at about 10 ft centres, every third one resting on a column; the intermediate two rest on the arcade girders but project below these to meet the ribs in the adjacent span.

The roof covering was originally framed in timber and was a mixture of slates on boarding and saw tooth roof glazing with wood bars. The latter has been replaced over the years by patent glazing in longitudinal runs. The original heavy wooden end screens with radial glazing bars survived two World Wars but without the glass. They have since been carefully replaced and reglazed with aluminium bars, preserving the radial pattern.

The new station took about three years to build and the roof is considered to be one of the best of its kind: it is of much later vintage than Paddington, which perhaps it most resembles, and 30 years later than Newcastle Central.[6]

The drawings for the contract with John Keswick in 1874 are signed by Benjamin Burleigh, the North Eastern Railway Architect.

10. Lendal Bridge, York   (HEW 209)   SE 599 519

The Minster can be seen from York Station and the direct half mile or so of road between them is carried over the River Ouse by Lendal Bridge. This was designed by Thomas Page of Westminster and opened in 1863. It has a single main span of 175 ft clear by 37 ft wide in the form of a Tudor arch with heraldic decoration and ornamental lamp standards. It is of cast iron, with six plain ribs each in eleven segments, made by Hawks Crawshay and Co. of Gateshead. Three additional ribs of steel were inserted in 1910 to permit the running of street tramcars which have long since disappeared.

This is quite a beautiful bridge as seen from the river banks, which are easily accessible. The City Walls terminate there at two towers, a small round one with conical tiled roof called Barker Tower on the station side and a larger square one on the Minster side known as Lendal Tower. At one time, from 1380 to 1538, a chain was stretched between the two to complete the City defences, and before the bridge was built the crossing was by boat at St Leonard's ferry.

The arch adjacent to Barker Tower is by G.T. Andrews for the

Great North of England Railway. Lendal Tower was from 1677 for many years the 'Waterhouse', where water was abstracted from the river, pumped to a roof tank and distributed in the City via wooden pipes. John Smeaton, the great civil engineer, was an active shareholder from 1779 and employed his talents in 1784 to improve the Newcomen engine there, traces of which remain.

11. York Waterworks, Acomb Landing   (HEW 216)
SE 582 525

In 1846 a new and much larger water supply for York was established a mile or so upstream, not far from the present Clifton Bridge. Thomas Hawksley (later to become President of the Institution of Civil Engineers in 1871) positioned the intake above the important Holgate Beck and set up a purification works, pumps, storage tanks and so on between the river and the main line railway to the north. James Simpson (President of the Institution in 1853) was called in to install some slow sand filters on the lines of those he had designed for the Chelsea Works in 1828. The contract drawings for York are signed by Simpson, and the work was constructed by James Darbyshire and Thomas Isaac. The design is for a rectangular settling basin about 200 ft by 90 ft with sloping sides, paved throughout. Water is introduced by central fountains and attains a depth of about 6 ft above successive layers of sand and gravel above tiles and drains.

This type of filter is very much slower than the modern mechanical filters, and occupies much more space, and now only one is left. It is however considered to be very effective and is being retained and improved.

12. Thornton Bridge   (HEW 17)   SE 433 715
The River Ouse above York is fed by the Ure and the Swale. Anyone who finds Lendal Bridge attractive should go to Helperby to see another example of the skill of Thomas Page of London. It was built by Keswick, presumably John Keswick who built York Station, with iron work by Swingler, and opened on 4 April 1865. A Mr Palliser was paid 8s 6d for taking photographs of the new bridge under construction.

It has a span of 98 ft and four cast iron girders of five segments forming slightly pointed arches. The ribs are of an unusual twin

Figure 4/4. York Station roof (British Rail)

Figure 4/5. Spa Bridge, Scarborough (Scarborough Borough Council)

form and perforated. The spandrels are the X-type lattice with large heraldic shields (York City) for which £20 was paid in 1867. The decorative quality is rather higher than one might expect in such a rural situation, although not far away at Myton on Swale a rather similar bridge, privately owned, displays much the same features in a more modest way.

13. Stamford Bridge Viaduct   (HEW 526)   SE 708 554

Much less ornate is the river span of the disused railway viaduct at Stamford Bridge between York and Hull. The 15 other spans are plain semi-circular 24 ft brick arches, and there is talk of demolition. The main point of interest is that this 90 ft span by 12 ft rise, six rib, five segment cast iron arch happens now to be about the oldest remaining railway bridge of this type. There are older cast iron bridges built for rail vehicles but these were on waggonways or narrow gauge lines.

The ribs here are plain 28 in deep with X-type spandrel bracing. The Engineer was J.C. Birkinshaw (1811–67) and the contractors Jackson and Bean (substructure) and Gilkes Wilson and Co., Middlesbrough (ironwork). The railway was opened on 4 October 1847.

14. Spa Bridge, Scarborough   (HEW 211)   TA 044 882
Figure 4/5

Perhaps a better attempt to combine style with simplicity is the four-span carriage drive, now limited to pedestrian use, near the Grand Hotel at Scarborough. Multiple span cast iron arches are rare, and this one dates from 1827. It is said to have been designed by one Outhett, and built by Stead, Snowden and Buckley. It has four spans of 66 ft 6 in by 22 ft wide with four ribs and radial spandrel members similar to the late Dunham Toll Bridge and other bridges by George Leather of Leeds. The piers are of ashlar neatly panelled and moulded, again very similar to Dunham.

15. Sea Cut, Scalby   (HEW 137)   SE 972 884 to TA 036 908

At the other end of Scarborough, at Scalby Mills, is the outlet to a civil engineering work of a different kind. The River Derwent rises on Fylingdales Moor, famous for its radar domes and for its geological interest relative to the Ice Age. Starting as it does close to the sea at Whitby, the Derwent flows south, then west to Stamford Bridge near York, then south to the Ouse at Barmby, thence into the Humber and east to the sea at Spurn, a very considerable diversion.

The area north of the A170 Pickering to Scarborough road at West Ayton is known as the High Lands. From there, south and west to Malton, the Low Lands are flat, and had for a long time suffered from flooding when heavy rain on the moors was impeded by silt and meanderings lower down.

The usual conflicting interests of mills and farms and of navigation below Malton, delayed an effective remedy until the year 1800, when agreement was reached to adopt William Chapman's scheme for an overflow from Weirhead at Everley to the sea at Scalby Mills, some 5 miles, known as the Sea Cut. The bed width is 30 ft, the fall 135 ft, there are ten weirs and four highway bridges. J. and F. Pinkerton carried out the earthwork, John King the bridges, and the weir at Everley was started by E. and R. Coates, and finished by J. and T. Hovington.

Sea Cut was opened on 3 September 1804 and, apart from its engineering interest, is worth a visit because of the attractive countryside in which it lies.

16. Suspension footbridge, Huttons Ambo   (HEW 789)
SE 765 677
The course of the River Derwent below Malton is very picturesque and as frequently happens the best view is from the railway. The railway station at Castle Howard, once used by Queen Victoria, was itself picturesque, as may be seen from the main station buildings which survive as a private house.

The nearby station of Huttons Ambo (also closed) had a special access across the river in the form of a suspension footbridge of 95 ft 6 in span built in 1886 which still survives. The A-frame pylons made of old permanent way rails are a notable feature.

17. Suspension footbridge, Grosmont   (HEW 790)
NZ 828 052
A similar bridge exists at Grosmont near Whitby over the Esk. This has a span of 54 ft and leads to the original small bore tunnel on the Pickering–Whitby horse worked railway.

18. Grosmont (horse) tunnel   (HEW 3)   NZ 827 051
Figure 4/6

The country between Pickering and Whitby (the North Yorks Moors) is even more picturesque, and George Stephenson's little horse drawn railway of 1836 blended well into the landscape. Quite sharp curves were good enough for the low speeds involved and the earthworks and structures were minimal considering the terrain. The larger bridges were of timber and have been replaced. This little tunnel 130 yd long by 10 ft wide by 14 ft high was replaced by a larger tunnel alongside when steam traction was introduced in 1847, but it remains in use to carry a footpath.

Frederick Swanwick was the site engineer and the portals were given the enhancement of turrets and castellations which, on this miniature scale, is unusual if not unique.

The change of ownership of the railway here is also notable, namely Whitby and Pickering, 1836
        York and North Midland, 1847
        North Eastern, 1854
        London and North Eastern, 1923
        British Transport Commission, 1947
        North York Moors Railway, 1973

Figure 4/6. Grosmont Tunnel (K. Hoole)

19. 'Scales' Bridge, Goathland   (HEW 826)   NZ 831 021

Also on the North York Moors Railway just north of Goathland is a metal bridge of some technical interest. It carries the line over Ellerbeck just north of the three-arch road bridge at Darnholme.

The original Whitby to Pickering Railway included a rope worked incline at Beckhole which was bypassed in 1864 by a 4 mile diversion. This was midway through the era of wrought iron railway bridges when the use of cast iron had not been quite discontinued. It was not unusual for a plate girder, a truss girder, or a tied arch to have a cast iron compression flange and a wrought iron tension flange or tie. 'Scales' bridge, number 30, is one such bridge which has survived, albeit stiffened by rolled steel channels in the top flange and strengthened by the addition of a new steel underslung centre girder in 1908.

The original bridge had two outer main girders and underslung cross girders carrying two tracks on longitudinal timbers. The bridge is on such a skew that only half the cross girders are full length. The old main girders are 90 ft long and hogbacked 4 ft to 7 ft deep. The bottom flange plates and angles, the web, and the web stiffeners are wrought iron, while the top flange is of cast iron cruciform section in lengths of about 12 ft with end plates for bolting together and through the web stiffeners. There is another similar bridge on the Esk Valley line from Middlesbrough to Whitby.

20. Knaresborough Viaduct   (HEW 153)   SE 348 571

Altogether different is the much illustrated railway viaduct over the River Nidd at Knaresborough. Designed explicitly to blend with an already picturesque ancient town, church and castle on the high wooded banks of a bend in the river, it is perhaps one of the most successful attempts to combine decorative embellishments with pure engineering. It is satisfying as a part of the landscape and indeed enhances it without suggesting any mechanical intrusion. It was designed by Thomas Grainger of Edinburgh, most of whose viaducts are particularly graceful or of extremely high quality masonry work, or both. Considered simply as an engineering work, it is a tall, elegant bridge, apparently of three segmental, almost semicircular arches, to which architectural detail has been added, but not overdone. In fact, the viaduct has four 56 ft 9 in spans—

one being half hidden in the trees—and is 78 ft high. It was opened on 1 October 1851.

21. Cast Iron Girder Bridge over Milby Cut   (HEW 210)
SE 395 672 Site, SE 593 510 Ironwork

Knaresborough had at one time a great trade in linen. The Nidd was not suitable for transport, so much of it went by road to Boroughbridge and thence to the Ouse and down to York. The Ouse is still navigable today for seagoing ships as far as Selby and for smaller craft up to York and beyond. In the 18th century locks were built at Naburn and at Linton, and John Smeaton and other eminent engineers were engaged to improve the situation still further north. One of these schemes was Milby Cut, to by-pass a difficult section of the Ure at Boroughbridge and eventually to reach Ripon.

Milby Cut was opened on 31 October 1769, and was crossed by the Great North Road at the north end of Boroughbridge, necessitating a minor diversion and a small bridge. This bridge was widened soon after 1792 and had to be duplicated in 1942, so forming a small roundabout which is still there. The old bridge was strengthened then and reconstructed in 1946 and the modernised A1 road has since been diverted to by-pass the town altogether. One of the cast iron girders from the Milby Cut bridge was preserved and, because it was railway owned at the time, it was sent to the Queen Street Museum at York. It is now in the National Railway Museum. It is a curious little girder which may even predate those of Ironbridge, Coalbrookdale. This has been claimed but not proved.

The girder is an arched T beam 18 ft long, 16 ft span with an 8 in by ¾ in top flange and a depth of 23 in at the abutments and 9 in at the centre with a web thickness in excess of 2 in. When demolished the bridge was 25 ft wide and had ten cast iron girders (and the new intermediate rolled steel joists) supporting stone slabs 5 in to 6 in thick presumably through lead or hardwood packing.

22. York City Bond   (HEW 355)   SE 603 513
Downstream from Lendal Bridge is Ouse Bridge, rather a fine structure of three stone arches opened in 1820. The original Roman bridge was located between the two. Beyond Ouse Bridge is King's Staith on the left bank and Queen's Staith opposite, where

most of the waterborne trade has been handled over the years. Skeldergate Bridge, further downstream, also designed by the firm of Thomas Page and Son and executed in wrought iron and decorative cast iron, incorporated an opening span for this reason.

Nearby on the right bank is a red brick warehouse of some character. This is the York City Bond, which in 1873 replaced a 17th century warehouse (a building of less architectural merit, which nevertheless survived until about 1968).

A new and better warehouse had been urged for many years, and eventually plans were produced by George Styan, the City Surveyor, in 1872, and the building was brought into use on 26 May of the following year. This forms the three-storey portion of the building on the Ouse Bridge side and is about 90 ft by 60 ft with brick side walls and a line of 8 in diameter cast iron columns supporting seven bays of jack arched floor. There are three windows each side, a central opening to the river and a hipped roof on king post trusses.

It was in full use within three months and it was extended in 1875 towards Skeldergate Bridge in two storeys about 75 ft square in two portions, one 30 ft wide in two bays with 5½ in diameter cast iron columns and the other 45 ft wide with 7 in diameter columns. Wines and spirits were stored for many years, but latterly dry goods such as tea and coffee have been preferred. The last boat to unload there is said to have been a cargo of hazel nuts in 1956.

Cast iron work is by Bagshaw and Son of Batley and there is an interesting cast iron string to wooden stairs in one corner.

CHAPTER 5

Cumbria

THIS region lies between the Solway, the Irish Sea, Morecambe Bay and the Pennines. To the north lie Gretna, the Rivers Esk and Eden, and the western end of Hadrian's Wall near Carlisle. To the west are the flat lands between Silloth and Maryport, industrial 'West Cumberland' once rich in iron and coal, dotted with mines and blast furnaces around Workington and Whitehaven, and near Millom and Barrow in Furness. The production of steel rails continues at Workington, the last stronghold of the Bessemer process. To the south are the estuaries of the Duddon, Leven and Kent and to the east, the Lune Gorge and the Eden Valley. Between all these is the English Lake District.

Apart from docks, harbours and coastal defences, and a few major buildings in Carlisle, the civil engineer has mainly been concerned with inland transport.

Rennie's Lancaster Canal was continued northward from the Lune Aqueduct as far as Kendal. A short canal was built at Ulverston. Carlisle was linked with Port Carlisle near Bowness by a canal, most of which was later converted into a railway. There were alternative schemes for a canal or a railway between Carlisle and Newcastle; it was the latter that was built.

The main railways are the Lancaster and Carlisle of 1847 via Shap and Penrith, now the west coast main line electrified route, and the Settle and Carlisle Line of 1875. Both traverse magnificent scenery, but the later one was only achieved at the expense of formidable engineering works. Cross country routes developed mainly to supply the west Cumberland iron industry and involved some spectacular iron viaducts, all now demolished but still remembered.

As for roads, the Romans reached Carlisle via Stainmore; the old route to Furness from York is via Kirkby Lonsdale, and the northbound road from Lancaster, latterly the A6, shares the Lune

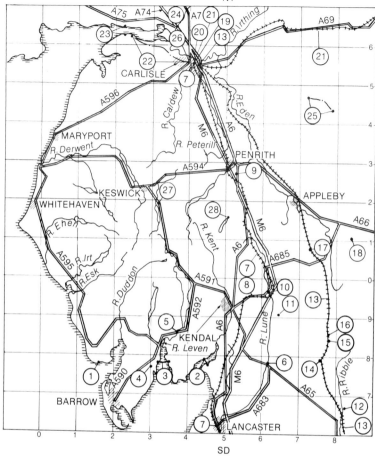

1. Hodbarrow Sea Barrier
2. Kent Viaduct
3. Leven Viaduct
4. Ulverston Canal
5. Newby Bridge
6. Devil's Bridge, Kirkby Lonsdale
7. Lancaster and Carlisle Railway
8. Dockray, Docker's Garth or Fiddler's Gill Viaduct
9. Lowther Viaduct
10. Lowgill Viaduct
11. Rawthey Viaduct
12. Stainforth Bridge, near Settle
13. Settle and Carlisle Railway

14. Ribblehead Viaduct
15. Dent Head Viaduct
16. Arten Gill Viaduct
17. Smardale Viaduct
18. Belah Viaduct
19. Carlisle Citadel Station
20. Carlisle Citadel Station roof
21. Newcastle and Carlisle Railway
22. Carlisle Canal
23. Solway Viaduct
24. Esk Viaduct or 'Metal Bridge'
25. Shaddon Mill, Carlisle
26. Nent Force Level
27. Thirlmere Dam
28. Haweswater Dam

Gorge and Shap Fell with the west coast main line railway and the
M6 motorway.

1. Hodbarrow Sea Barrier   (HEW 968)
SD 165 787 to SD 182 781

By 1840 the west coast rail route from London had reached
Liverpool, Preston and Lancaster. An extension to Carlisle was
mooted, via Kendal (already served by canal) and Shap, but the
mountain barrier was formidable.

Would it be feasible to cross Morecambe Bay and follow the
coast to Whitehaven? This was a longer route, but already partly
built, and it would take in several thriving small towns and ports.
George Stephenson was confident that embankments could be
built across the Kent, Leven and Duddon estuaries and that the
value of reclaimed land would offset the cost.

For a time the idea was supported and an even more ambitious
but less practicable scheme was evolved to go more or less directly
from Lancaster to Barrow. This proved too difficult and the direct
route via Oxenholme was revived.

In fact a modified version of Stephenson's three sea crossings
did eventually mature, Kent and Leven Viaducts being partly
embankments. Although not part of a railway scheme there was
also a notable land reclamation work built across the Duddon
Sands near Millom between 1900 and 1905 in connection with the
Hodbarrow Mines, now unfortunately (since 1968) disused. It was
a bank 7000 ft long from Haverigg to Hodbarrow Point, with a top
width of 83 ft, base width of 210 ft and height 40 ft. The triple
section included an outer rubble limestone and concrete block
bank, an inner one of limestone and the interior of puddle clay
and sheet piles. The Engineer was William Matthews and the
Contractor John Aird and Co; the cost was approximately
£500 000.[1]

2. Kent Viaduct   (HEW 963)   SD 453 792
3. Leven Viaduct   (HEW 964)   SD 322 787   Figure 5/1

Once the projects for routing the Anglo-Scottish traffic around the
coast of Furness and west Cumberland had been abandoned,
railways in that area were promoted with less urgency on a local
basis. It was not until 1857 that the Ulverstone and Lancaster
Railway reached the main line at Carnforth.

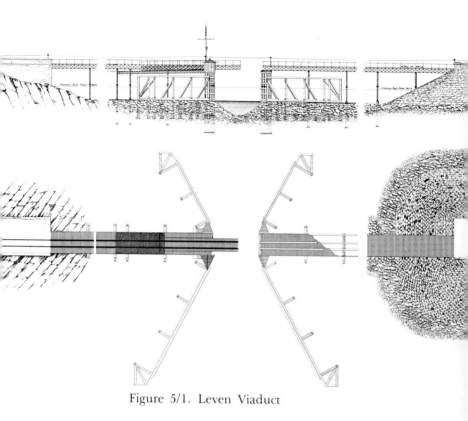

Figure 5/1. Leven Viaduct

Figure 5/2. Devil's Bridge, Kirkby Lonsdale

The main engineering works were the two long viaducts near Ulverston (Leven) and at Arnside (Kent).[2,3] They have been extensively reconstructed over the years but have several points of interest. Both have a considerable number of short spans—Kent had 50 at 30 ft centres and an opening span of 36 ft clear; Leven had 48 at 30 ft and an opening span of 36 ft clear. The movable spans were telescopic and necessitated by shipping movements which had ceased commercially by 1866.

James Brunlees was the Engineer and he had to deal with difficult conditions of sand and silt (up to 70 ft deep) and with the speed and range of tides. He used cast iron piles and 10 in diameter columns with large discs at the base. There were initially four columns per pier for a single track railway, increased to six when the second track was added in 1863. The cast iron deteriorated in the estuarine conditions and the piles were enclosed in brick and concrete in about 1915. The original wrought iron lattice girders, one under each rail, were replaced in 1885–7 and some spans have since been altered.

At the Leven Viaduct a minor version of the Tay Bridge disaster occurred on 27 February 1903, when the mail train was blown over in a high wind. Fortunately it stayed on the bridge, which was undamaged, and there was no loss of life. A special wind gauge was installed soon after, modelled on one at Barmouth, and connected to the adjacent signal boxes.

4. Ulverston Canal (HEW 619) SD 293 785 to SD 314 776
Not far away is the Ulverston (Ship) Canal which was built by John Rennie in 1793–6, disused in 1916, abandoned in 1945, and is now an industrial reservoir.

5. Newby Bridge (HEW 677) SD 369 863
The River Leven is the southern overflow from Lake Windermere, and at Newby Bridge near Lakeside is a much older and more imposing bridge than Leven Viaduct. It is one of the finest ancient road bridges in the district and has five segmental arches with massive cutwaters and recesses at road level. An even finer one is to be seen at Kirkby Lonsdale.

6. Devil's Bridge, Kirkby Lonsdale (HEW 147)
SD 616 782 Figure 5/2
For a period of some six centuries the River Lune has been crossed

at Kirkby Lonsdale by a structure known as the Devil's Bridge, supposedly built by the monks of St. Mary's Abbey, York, the owners of lands to the west of it. It is constructed of three spans, two of 55 ft and one of 28 ft; height of the parapet from water level is 45 ft and each arch exhibits four ribs, the same type of construction as found at Twizel. Having a width between parapets of only 11 ft 7 in the bridge was closed to traffic in 1932 and is now preserved as an ancient monument.

7. Lancaster and Carlisle Railway   (HEW 958)
SD 472 617 to NY 402 555

It was the possibilities of the Lune Gorge which convinced Joseph Locke that a main line railway to Carlisle could be routed up and over the hills. A Royal Commission was also in favour of a direct route through or near Kendal. Several alternatives were considered, including a lengthy tunnel, but eventually the two rising gradients of 13 miles from Milnthorpe to Grayrigg at 1 in 173, 111, 106 and of 5 miles from Tebay to Shap Summit, at 1 in 145 and 1 in 75 were considered practicable enough for the locomotive power and train loads then available.

The railway was built to cross the old main road near Tewitfield and run closely to the east of it past Kendal (served by a branch line from Oxenholme), then swing to the right with the A685 Kirkby Stephen road across the high ground to Grayrigg. From Low Gill to Tebay the railway now shares the Lune Gorge with the river, the M6 and the A685 and has easier gradients. Indeed at Dillicar it was possible to site locomotive pick-up water troughs in later steam days.

From Tebay there was no option but to climb the valley of the Birk Beck to Shap Summit 914 ft above sea level. This punishing 4 miles at 1 in 75 meant that banking engines had to be kept at Tebay to assist heavy trains up to Shap, a practice which continued until the line was electrified in 1974. To compare railway gradients with road gradients a factor of 10 is appropriate, for instance 1 in 7 on the road and 1 in 70 on the railway are roughly comparable.

From Kendal to Shap the old A6 keeps to higher ground and has always been more susceptible to blockage by snow in winter than has the railway, as indeed is the Settle and Carlisle line a few miles to the east.

The railway descends to the Lowther and Eamont valleys at

Penrith and thence runs in easier territory to Carlisle. Apart from a few modest viaducts the engineering works were relatively slight. Joseph Locke and the contractors John Stephenson and Mackenzie and Brassey completed the work between 1844 and 1846. This was the first of three races against time with the east coast route via York, Newcastle and Berwick-upon-Tweed. The latter was mainly complete well ahead of the west coast route but was eventually delayed by the need to build major viaducts across the rivers Tyne and Tweed.

The second race was in 1888 in a competition to cut the time of ten hours from London to Edinburgh. The third, in 1895, after the opening of the Forth Bridge and Tay Bridge, was a race to Aberdeen, actually a series of races. In one of these (on 22 August) the small 2–4–0 Precedent locomotive *Hardwicke* built at Crewe in 1892, to the designs of F.W. Webb, went up the 5½ mile Shap gradient in 6 min, which was no mean feat for those days. The 141 miles from Crewe to Carlisle were covered at an average speed of 67 mile/h.

This locomotive is still in steam and is preserved at the National Railway Museum in York. An excellent description of working a steam locomotive up Shap is given by Tuplin.[4]

8. Dockray, Docker's Garth, or Fiddler's Gill Viaduct
(HEW 596)   SD 566 957
9. Lowther Viaduct   (HEW 597)   NY 525 270
10. Lowgill Viaduct   (HEW 721)   SD 616 965

The first of these three viaducts is near Grayrigg summit, over a tributary of the river Mint, and has six arches of 50 ft. The second, over the river Lowther near Penrith, has six arches of 60 ft and is 110 ft high.

Although the original Lancaster and Carlisle Railway viaducts with their tapered piers are very graceful, it is the Lowgill Viaduct, now disused, on the Ingleton Branch, which can best be seen from the train in a magnificent setting. It dates from 1857 and not only has restrained decoration which gives it character, but it is larger than the main line viaducts, having eleven arches of 45 ft span and is 88 ft high. J. Errington, who was Locke's assistant on the main Lancaster and Carlisle Railway, was Engineer.

The Ingleton Branch (London and North Western Railway) linked up with the Midland Railway line from Skipton to

Morecambe and might well have become a major route to Scotland, via the Lancaster and Carlisle Railway had not the Midland Railway been eventually forced to build their own Settle and Carlisle line. The Ingleton line was eventually closed in 1967 but two very fine masonry and cast iron arch bridges remain, one over the river Lune at SD 630 930 about two miles north of Sedbergh, and the other (HEW 723) one mile south of Sedbergh over the Rawthey.

11. Rawthey Viaduct   (HEW 723)   SD 643 909

This is a very fine structure indeed with heavy masonry abutments neatly adorned with simple copings and strings and a dentil course. The 124 ft cast iron arch span is on a 40° skew and has four ribs with a 26 ft rise and 3 ft 3 in depth at crown. The spandrels are filled with tall round-headed cast iron arcades on two tiers. The bridge was 26 ft 6 in wide for two tracks and 48 ft from rail level to water level, but most of the decking has been removed and the bridge is now used to carry public utilities.

12. Stainforth Bridge, near Settle   (HEW 4)   SD 818 672

While there are many ancient road bridges older and more interesting architecturally than this, as a pack horse bridge of 17th century vintage it has the engineering features of a relatively large span over a major river (the Ribble) on a major route (York to Lancaster) and the added interest that since 1931 it has belonged to the National Trust.

It is narrow and hump backed over a plain parallel ring segmental arch with 3 ft parapets, all in dry stone with no embellishments, yet most attractive.

13. Settle and Carlisle Line   (HEW 959)
SD 813 610 to NY 402 555

In its heyday the Midland Railway, centred on Derby, extended to all four corners of the country, either on its own metals or jointly with other railways. Its London extension to St. Pancras came rather late, as it had previously co-operated with the London and North Western Railway (Euston) and Great Northern Railway (King's Cross).

Leeds and Bradford were on the Midland Railway system and York was reached over the old York and North Midland section of the North Eastern Railway. A branch to Skipton, Settle, Lancaster and Morecambe brought the Midland within reach of Cumbria, and another branch from Clapham Junction (Yorks) to Ingleton made through running possible to Scotland over the Lancaster and Carlisle line of the London and North Western Railway.

Congestion on the Shap route and railway politics inevitably forced the Midland to project its own route between Skipton and Carlisle over the toughest part of the Pennines. The earlier railways had naturally used the easiest locations already so the new Midland Region line via Settle, Ribblehead, Garsdale, Kirkby Stephen and Appleby involved a long drag up gradients of 1 in 100 to an 1169 ft summit at Ais Gill.[5 6] There are twice as many viaducts as on the Shap route, and bigger ones at that, together with a dozen tunnels, one of them (Blea Moor) being 2629 yd long and with shafts 500 ft deep. Cuttings and embankments are on an enormous scale, and when the new line was opened in 1876 passengers found it to be one of the most magnificent scenic routes in the country. The southern half is stern, bare and bleak with views of Ingleborough at 2373 ft, Pen-y-ghent at 2273 ft and Great Whernside at 2419 ft. The northern part down the valley of the Eden is softer but equally beautiful.

14. Ribblehead Viaduct   (HEW 6)   SD 759 795
This is the largest of the viaducts and easily viewed from the B6255 road near Ingleton. It has 24 arches of 45 ft span in four groups of six on a curve of 68 chains radius and is over 100 ft high.

15. Dent Head Viaduct   (HEW 7)   SD 777 844
This ten arch viaduct 100 ft high is just over 250 miles from St Pancras Station. It is best seen from Newby Head road and, with the adjacent Arten Gill Viaduct, gives an excellent impression of the wild country through which the Settle and Carlisle Line, this magnificent piece of Victorian railway engineering, had to pass.

The Viaduct is about 1150 ft above sea level and the view down the vale towards Dent village is one of the highlights of the railway journey. The station was scarcely adjacent to the village, being four miles from and 500 ft above it. In the village itself is an interesting memorial to the eminent geologist Alan Sedgwick (1785–1873).

16. Arten Gill Viaduct   (HEW 8)   SD 777 859   Figure 5/3

This has 11 spans of 45 ft in groups of two, three and six, separated by stop piers. The height is 117 ft from rail to water level and some piers are recorded as being 55 ft deep to the foundations, containing stone blocks up to 8 tons in weight.

17. Smardale Viaduct   (HEW 960)   NY 732 081

Of the many viaducts on this line, this one is notable as being at 130 ft the highest on the Midland Railway and for including a tablet 6 ft long inscribed 'laid by Agnes Crossley 8 June 1875'. Mrs Crossley was the wife of the Midland Railway Chief Engineer at that time, John Crossley.

The viaduct spanned not only Scandal Beck but the South Durham and Lancashire Union Railway, that is, the line from Kirkby Stephen to Tebay. This North Eastern Railway branch was part of the Stockton and Darlington Railway development to serve Barrow-in-Furness and west Cumberland. Material for the construction of the Midland Railway Smardale Viaduct was brought to site on this route, which has now been abandoned. Kirkby Stephen is nearby to the east, and beyond it again is the site of the famous Belah Viaduct.

18. Belah Viaduct   (HEW 967)   NY 839 105   Figure 5/4

The South Durham and Lancashire Union Railway (Furness was then part of Lancashire) was opened in 1861. It climbed even higher than the Settle and Carlisle line as the summit at Stainmore was at 1378 ft above sea level, the highest railway in England.

The Engineer was Thomas Bouch and, unlike the Engineer on the Midland Railway line 15 years later, he decided to use iron trestle structures for his viaducts at Belah and Deepdale. The advantage was that factory-made components could be brought to site by rail and erected quickly. Belah was in fact 16 spans of 60 ft with a maximum height of 196 ft and built in four months. It had stone abutments and pier bases with six-leg trestles of cast iron flanged pipes of 12 in diameter, bolted and braced with wrought iron tie bars in panels 15 ft high. The towers were 14 ft by 22 ft at the top, with outside legs raked at 1 in 12 giving a maximum width of 48 ft at the base.

'Lattice' (double Warren) girders in three lines with timber deck carried at first single, and later double, track. The girders were strengthened in 1899 and overhauled in 1933. Increasing age and maintenance costs coupled with decreasing traffic forced the closure of the line in 1962 and with the demolition of Belah and Deepdale two of the most notable viaducts of their type disappeared.

19. Carlisle Citadel Station   (HEW 537)   NY 402 555

As one of the principal links in the system of the west coast route to Scotland, Carlisle Citadel Station was originally built to serve the Lancaster and Carlisle and the Caledonian Railways, and was opened in 1847. The main station buildings were designed by William Tite (1798–1873)—later Sir William—and the frontage, overlooking Court Square, has been described as a fine example of 16th century collegiate railway architecture. Constructed by John Stephenson and 470 ft long it includes a portico on which are displayed the heraldic devices adopted by the Lancaster and Carlisle and the Caledonian Railways.

It was originally intended that the Newcastle and Carlisle and the Maryport and Carlisle Railway arms should be displayed as these companies were involved in the negotiations for a joint Station. Eventually no fewer than seven pre-amalgamation railways used it, namely: Newcastle and Carlisle, open 1838 to London Road, transferred to Citadel 1863; Maryport and Carlisle, open 1845 to Crown Street, transferred to Citadel 1851; Lancaster and Carlisle, open 1846 initially to London Road, transferred to Citadel 1847; Caledonian, open 1847 to Citadel; Glasgow and South Western open 1849, into Citadel over Caledonian Railway metals 1851; North British, open 1864 to Citadel; Midland (Settle and Carlisle), open 1876 to Citadel.[7]

20. Carlisle Citadel Station Roof   (HEW 437)   NY 402 555
Figure 5/5

The opening of the Settle and Carlisle line brought additional main line traffic into the Joint Citadel Station at Carlisle. Additional tracks, platforms and buildings became necessary and the present station roof, a listed structure, was constructed as part of this enlargement scheme. Of iron and glass, the roof originally covered an overall area of 6½ acres and it was carried on 26 deep lattice or double Warren girders at 40 ft centres, each with ten panels,

Figure 5/3. Arten Gill Viaduct (British Rail)

Figure 5/4. Belah Viaduct (British Rail)

Figure 5/5. Carlisle Citadel Station roof

stiffened end posts and a flat bottom tie. The spaces between the girders are filled with balanced cantilevered half-trusses at approximately 12 ft centres, the roof covering being mainly patent glazing. The whole effect is of extreme lightness and yet ample strength. Much of the roof, including the Gothic end screens, was removed in 1958. The Engineers were Blythe and Cunningham.

21. Newcastle and Carlisle Railway   (HEW 962)
NZ 245 637 to NY 403 554

The Newcastle and Carlisle Railway originated with proposals made as early as 1776 for a canal. Unusually, William Chapman was involved later with proposals for both a canal and the railway; he was joint engineer when the prospectus for the railway was first published in 1825. Work on the construction of the railway began in 1829 under the direction of Francis Giles and under him the four principal works at the line's western end were constructed. They are the Wetheral (NY 469 546) and Corby (NY 473 548) viaducts, the Gelt Bridge (NY 532 573) and the Cowran cutting. This cutting is a mile long, half of it being 100 ft deep with walls 14 ft high for most of that. It is about 8 miles from Carlisle.

The Wetheral viaduct consists of five semi-circular arches each of

80 ft span, the railway being carried at a height of 93 ft across the river Eden. Iron cantilevers carry a footbridge on the north face of the viaduct. The comparable statistics for the Corby viaduct are seven arches of 40 ft with a height of 60 ft. Both structures are of red sandstone with piers 25 ft wide and each has a width between parapets of 22 ft. The contractor was William Denton.

Some five miles to the east of the Eden crossing is the Gelt Bridge, a 27° skew bridge with three arches each of 30 ft carrying the twin tracks at a height of 60 ft above the river; it was built by John McKay.

During the construction of the railway Giles was superseded by John Blackmore, and it was not until June 1838 that the complete length of the railway, 63 miles, was opened.[8,9]

22. Carlisle Canal   (HEW 969)
NY 391 560 to NY 241 622

In 1818 a proposal for a canal between Carlisle and the Solway was made by William Chapman. His proposals were incorporated in the Act of Parliament which was passed the following year; construction began almost immediately and the canal was completed in 1823. It was 11½ miles long and included six locks and two basins in its length, together with the terminal basin in Carlisle, the latter being connected later by rail to the Newcastle and Carlisle Railway.

The locks were 74 ft by 17 ft and were capable of passing barges of up to 100 tons. Water was supplied from a reservoir near Kirkandrews and, by pumping, from the river Eden. From the basin at Carlisle the canal pursued a westerly course to Drumburgh, then turned north west to Port Carlisle near Bowness on Solway. It achieved a modest success until the coming of railways and indeed contributed to their adoption by conveying the locomotive *Rocket* on its way from Newcastle by road, canal and sea to Liverpool for the 1829 Rainhill Trials.

In 1853–4 the Carlisle Canal was converted to a railway and the canal drawbridges were replaced by cast iron girder bridges, several of which remain. The railway goods shed of the later railway still stands in Carlisle, built upon the former canal basin. As a railway, from 1856 the main line ran to new docks at Silloth and the section between Drumbrugh and Port Carlisle became a branch line, which was worked until 1914 by a horse-drawn passenger coach now preserved in York Railway Museum. The undertaking eventually became part of the North British Railway.

The canal warehouse built in 1821 at the Carlisle basin was demolished in 1974, but the coal and lime vaults remain; at Port Carlisle the warehouses have been converted into houses and many of the lock and bridge-keepers' houses still remain.

23. Solway Viaduct   (HEW 714)
NY 212 628 to NY 206 643

Port Carlisle was obliged to close in 1868 when one of the longest railway viaducts in Europe was built across the Solway downstream and without an opening span. It connected the two Scottish railways, the Caledonian at Kirtlebridge and the Glasgow and South Western at Annan, with the iron works in west Cumberland via the Silloth Branch and the Maryport and Carlisle Railway.

It was 5790 ft long with 181 piers and designed by James Brunlees who also built the Kent and Leven Viaducts. It had five-column braced trestle piers and 30 ft span plate girders. It was opened to goods traffic in 1869 and to passenger traffic in 1870. In 1875–6 it was damaged and in 1881 partially destroyed by ice floes (45 piers and 37 spans) but was repaired and reopened in 1884. It was disused in 1921 and demolished in 1934–5.

24. Esk Viaduct or Metal Bridge   (HEW 970)   NY 355 649
Another structure long since demolished is Telford's cast iron three-arch bridge over the river Esk some six miles north of Carlisle on the A74. It was replaced by a modern structure in 1916 but a section of the parapet is preserved in the Tullie House Museum, as is the name 'Metal Bridge' on the map. The 1916 bridge was replaced in 1974.

Telford's bridge had three spans of 150, 105 and 105 ft, a somewhat unusual arrangement, and was erected in 1820.

25. Shaddon Mill, Carlisle   (HEW 961)   NY 395 556
Figure 5/6

This building dominates the skyline in Carlisle.

At the time of its completion in 1836 Shaddon Mill was said to be the largest cotton mill in England. The seven-storey mill building is 225 ft long by 60 ft wide and 83 ft high, with a chimney towering above it to a height of 305 ft. The mill was built for Peter

Figure 5/6. Shaddon Mill

Dixon, at one time employing 8000 people in the area, and its design was by Robert Tattersall with the interior cast iron framing and machinery designed by William Fairbairn. The main beams span 18 ft between 6½ in diameter columns; the beams are spaced at 9 ft 3 in centres. Shallow brick vaulting carries tiled floors with 10 ft 6 in headroom.

26. Nent Force Level   (HEW 398)
NY 719 468 to NY 783 436
An interesting classic no longer in existence is the Nent Force Level.[10]

During the eighteenth century, and well into the nineteenth, lead mining was a thriving industry in Cumberland, as it was the length of the Pennines. In the Alston area the terrain was suitable for draining a number of mines by means of a 'level' that is, a main drainage tunnel leading to an outlet at natural ground level.

In 1776 John Smeaton began the construction of such a drainage level from Alston to Nenthead, a distance of nearly five miles. In addition to providing drainage for lead mines, the Nent Force Level was of such a size that it could be used for transporting, by boats up to 30 ft long, the ores from the face. A third reason for its construction was that it might act as an exploratory tunnel, so enabling further mineral deposits to be located. In fact it was only successful in its purpose as a means of drainage.

The tunnel was not completed until 1842 and it included six shafts along its length; the cross section was some 9 ft square with a water depth of 5 ft. Although the level is now inaccessible, a commemorative stone has been placed in the Town Hall at Alston.

27. Thirlmere Dam   (HEW 607)   NY 308 189

Although perhaps not outstanding examples of dams in the United Kingdom, Thirlmere and Haweswater Dams can scarcely be omitted from a review of civil engineering work in the English Lake District.

Thirlmere dates from 1894 when the St John's Beck, a tributary of the Greta south of Keswick, was dammed to provide a reservoir for the Manchester Corporation (now the North West Water Authority). The lake was more than doubled in area and the water level raised, eventually by 50 ft.

The dam is some 65 ft high with a crest length of 740 ft and was designed by G.H. Hill and Sons and built by Morrison and Mason. The water is conveyed to Manchester by a 95 mile aqueduct.[11,12]

28. Haweswater Dam   (HEW 181)   NY 504 157   Figure 5/7

Also built for Manchester Corporation Water Works (by direct

Figure 5/7. Haweswater Dam (North West Water Authority)

labour), and now the responsibility of the North West Water Authority, this dam retains a volume of water twice that of Thirlmere. It was built between 1934–41 and hence is of an age which would not normally qualify as an Historical Engineering Work. It is a mass concrete buttress dam, the first of its type in this country, with a crest length of 1540 ft and is 120 ft high. It consists of 44 separate concrete blocks each 35 ft wide, solid for the top 20 ft then splitting into two legs to form an inverted V with feet 112 ft apart at the base of the dam. This dam can be seen in the distance from the train near Shap.

The lake was thereby raised by nearly 100 ft, increasing its length from 2½ miles to 4 miles. The outlet is by one of the longest tunnels of its kind.[13]

CHAPTER 6

South and West Yorkshire

SOUTH of York are the flat lands, occupied by the lower reaches of the rivers Derwent, Ouse, Aire and Don. All these are or have been navigable, joining as the Ouse with the Trent near Goole to form the Humber. Hidden below ground are what are now regarded as the best parts of the Barnsley seam of coal. Further west are the traditional coalfields of Yorkshire which for centuries have served both local industries and the export markets to London and abroad, latterly via Goole and Hull. The natural waterways were first improved and later augmented by canals to handle this traffic, some of it westwards over or through the Pennines. The Aire and Calder Navigation is one such waterway whose policy of extensive modernisation involving heavy engineering works has kept it commercially viable.

The difficult terrain delayed the spread of railways for a while; they brought with them a vast number of large viaducts and long tunnels. Even the very early Leeds and Selby Railway, in nearly flat territory, has considerable civil engineering interest, not least for the fact that it was the work of James Walker, second President of the Institution of Civil Engineers, and that it skirts the village near Leeds where John Smeaton lived and is now buried.

In his Presidential address in 1966, the 101st holder of that office made an interesting analysis of his predecessors, including their birthplaces. Nine came from Yorkshire, among them Joseph Locke, the great railway engineer, who was born in Sheffield and became the ninth President, and Sir John Hawkshaw, from Otley, who dominated the profession in the 1860s and 1870s and became the eleventh President. He is perhaps best remembered for the construction of the Severn Tunnel, but he was also Chief Engineer or Consulting Engineer to the Lancashire and Yorkshire Railway for over 50 years.

Equally famous was Sir John Fowler (thirteenth President) born

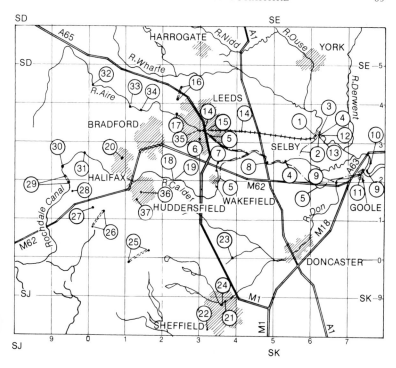

1. Abbots Staith Warehouse, Selby
2. Selby Canal and Swing Bridge
3. Selby Toll Bridge
4. Beal Bridge
5. Aire and Calder Navigation
6. Middleton Colliery Railway, Leeds
7. Stanley Ferry Aqueduct
8. Brotherton Bridge
9. Dutch River
10. Goole Swing Bridge
11. Water Towers, Goole
12. Selby Swing Bridge, East Coast Main Line Railway
13. Selby Station roof
14. Leeds and Selby Railway
15. Richmond Hill Tunnel, Leeds
16. Bramhope Tunnel
17. Cast iron arch bridge, Newlay and Horsforth
18. Cast iron arch bridge No. 6, Thornhill
19. Cast iron arch bridge No. 8, Thornhill
20. North Bridge, Halifax
21. Norfolk Bridge, Sheffield
22. Abbeydale Industrial Hamlet, Sheffield
23. Elsecar Colliery pumping engine
24. Wicker Arches, Sheffield
25. Woodhead Tunnels
26. Standedge Tunnels
27. March Haigh Dam
28. Roman Road, Blackstone Edge
29. Summit Tunnel
30. Gauxholme Viaduct, Todmorden
31. Old Hebden Bridge
32. Kildwick Bridge
33. Bingley Five Rise Locks
34. Salt's Mill, Saltaire
35. Leeds Corn Exchange
36. Station buildings, Huddersfield
37. Lockwood Viaduct, Huddersfield

in Sheffield, trained under J.T. Leather of Leeds, and especially remembered for his association with Sir Benjamin Baker on the design and construction of the Forth Railway Bridge.

The nineteenth President, J.F. la Trobe Bateman of Halifax, was very well known in the field of water supply.

William Chapman was born in Whitby and made his name in building canals and harbours and in land drainage before the Institution was even founded. Sir Edward Banks, of Richmond, Yorkshire, was of the same generation; he was a noted civil engineering contractor and was knighted in 1822.

1. Abbots Staith Warehouse, Selby   (HEW 782)
SE 616 326
As mentioned in the description of the Aire and Calder Navigation (HEW 294) Selby is an inland port on the River Ouse. It was an outlet for the products of the West Riding of Yorkshire long before the canal era and visible evidence of this remains.

Just upstream of the toll road bridge is a modern flour mill and jetty. Parts of the buildings furthest from the river are built in squared stone blocks and date from the 12th century. They are at the end of Micklegate, in a short street called the Quay, and were designated a Listed Building Grade II in 1952.

Not much is known about it, but the site is certainly called Abbots Staith and old maps show it to be the principal anchorage, perhaps because of the confluence of a watercourse known as Selby Dam. It is thought that stone, lead and iron for the construction of Selby Abbey were brought in at Abbots Staith and that subsequent trade was sufficient to justify quite large buildings for warehousing.

Water Street, Manchester, may well be the earliest railway warehouse extant: Abbots Staith is one of the oldest we have on our inland waterways.

2. Selby Canal and Swing Bridge   (HEW 785)   SE 621 320
Increasing production of coal and manufactured goods in the West Riding throughout the 18th century, coupled with the very unsatisfactory state of the roads at that time, encouraged the Aire and Calder Navigation to unceasing efforts to improve their waterway.

The lower reaches of the Aire were not at all satisfactory and the opening of a new turnpike road from Leeds to Selby in 1742 not only showed the need to eliminate the ferry across the Ouse there but persuaded the Aire and Calder Navigation to provide a 5 mile short cut from the Aire at Haddesley to the Ouse at Selby.

William Jessop was the Engineer and the canal was opened in 1778; it was successful for some time but was outmoded first by the next Aire and Calder Navigation major extension to Goole, and in 1834 by the opening of the Leeds and Selby Railway.

Selby Canal is still in use, if not commercially, and the tiny swing bridge at Selby is one of three to be seen in a radius of ½ mile. It was modernised as recently as 1977; before that it was like the toll bridge, of timber construction.

3. Selby Toll Bridge   (HEW 784)   SE 617 325

Toll bridges are not very popular in this country. Those who use them feel aggrieved that the local inhabitants have not provided them with a bridge free of cost, while the locals forget that their rates are lower than they might be.

Selby Toll Bridge is quite expensive to maintain. Not only does it carry a heavy road traffic, but the River Ouse is alive with shipping which is difficult to manoeuvre and frequently damages the substructure and protective fendering. The bridge itself was reconstructed in 1970.

There was a ferry at this point for 700 years. Road traffic was modest, being influenced by the volume of shipping proceeding upstream to York. Increasing traffic from Leeds to Abbots Staith spilled over to the Aire and Calder Navigation, whose Selby Canal outlet opened in 1778 bringing considerably more trade to Selby.

A census on the ferry traffic in 1790 showed that in one year 105 000 pedestrians, 75 000 horses, 30 000 farm animals and 500 vehicles were conveyed across the river. A report was commissioned from William Jessop on the possibility of a bridge, and this was authorised in 1791 after an exhaustive enquiry into a host of local objections. Some of the technical stipulations arising from this enquiry are incorporated in the Act which explains why a 1970 bridge looks more like a 1790 one. In fact both road width and waterway opening have been improved. There is a model of the old bridge in the Science Museum, South Kensington.

4. Beal Bridge   (HEW 787)   SE 533 255

Timber bridges, at one time almost universal, are now quite rare, even for temporary work. This one has no particular merit except as an example of a disappearing type. It has one main span over the navigational channel of the River Aire and three shorter spans each side on the rising gradients of the approaches. The piers are five-leg trestles with appropriate bracing to the bases and to stay the parapet fences. It carries a minor road in rural surroundings midway between Knottingley and the Haddlesey end of the Selby Canal.

5. Aire and Calder Navigation   (HEW 294)   SE 308 330
and SE 343 202 to SE 748 231

The Aire and Calder Navigation, now a part of the British Waterways Board, is of such historical interest and complexity as to be difficult to describe in a few paragraphs. It is not restricted to narrow boats and it has therefore avoided the inevitable commercial eclipse suffered by most British canals; it still carries freight. It originated in 1699 as a river navigation, that is with a ready-made waterway. It was strategically well placed to connect the mineral and industrial wealth of the West Riding to the River Ouse and the Humber ports. The timing was right; it had already prospered when much heavier demands began to be made upon it, so that the finance and the expertise were already there to meet the challenge.

The River Aire flows through the centre of Leeds and joins the Ouse at Airmyn near Goole. Wakefield, on the Calder, is virtually on a short branch from the Aire, at Castleford.

Rivers can be unpredictable, and the Aire and Calder Navigation history is one long list of widenings, deepenings, realignments and by-passes. John Smeaton and John Rennie were both involved at one time or another, while William Jessop built the Selby Canal.

By 1820 Telford was concerned in a very much more ambitious project. The upper parts of both the Aire and the Calder were drastically improved, and the lower Aire was by-passed completely by the Knottingley–Goole Canal and the establishment of Goole itself as a port in 1828. John Rennie was succeeded on this work by George Leather, of Leeds.

The Aire and Calder Navigation terminus at Leeds (SE 308 330) is connected to the Leeds and Liverpool Canal near the City railway station. The river itself is used for the first mile to Knostrop; the next six miles to Kippax are in cut, then the river is used again as far as Castleford (10 miles from Leeds). Here is the British Waterways Depot and a 'crossroads'. The Aire continues for a short arm in its old course but the main route is to the left in the Castleford Cut, opposite the River Calder which joins the Aire here as the fourth leg.

The Aire is used again past the Ferrybridge power stations (which are partly coaled from the Aire and Calder Navigation) and under the A1, the Great North Road. John Carr's rather splendid masonry arch bridge, now disused, is preserved close by the new reinforced concrete structure.

The Knottingley–Goole Canal then locks out to the right, quite close to the A1, but at Bank Dole Lock, 16½ miles from Leeds, there is a link to the river which is then navigable for 6½ miles to West Haddesley via Beal (HEW 787). From West Haddesley (within sight of Eggborough Power Station) the Selby Canal connects to the Ouse 11¾ miles from Bank Dole.

The Ouse is navigable at Selby by sea-going vessels although it is 16 miles above Goole, which is itself two hours by water from the sea. Aire and Calder Navigation traffic mainly continues from Knottingley via the 1826 cut through Whitley Bridge and Heck to Goole, (34 miles, SE 7523). The New Junction Canal of 1905 joins at 26¾ miles giving access to the Sheffield and South Yorkshire Navigation.

The other arm of the Aire and Calder Navigation is to Wakefield (SE 343 200) which is 8 miles from the Aire at Castleford. There is connection to the Calder and Hebble Navigation at Fall Ings Lock and the Barnsley Canal used to join in hereabouts too. The River Calder is completely by-passed for the next 5 miles by a cut which actually crosses it at Stanley Ferry (HEW 191). The last 2½ miles from Woodnook new cut to Castleford are in the river itself, after much improvement work.

One of the many notable features of the Aire and Calder Navigation is the compartment boat system, trains of 40 ton metal tubs hauled by a tug nineteen or so at a time, and individually hoisted and overturned mechanically at Goole for discharge to ship. The system was pioneered by the Aire and Calder Navigation engineer W.H. Bartholomew in 1862 and is still in use. Tubs of various sizes in varying numbers both pushed and pulled have been operated. A modern development is installed at Ferrybridge Electricity Generating Station where 170 ton craft in sets of three are brought from the colliery loading points down the canal to dock individually at Ferrybridge and be hoisted and discharged bodily at the waterside and inverted into the coal hoppers which are linked by conveyors to the power stations.

6. Middleton Colliery Railway, Leeds   (HEW 221)
SE 305 307

Not far from the Aire in Leeds is an important element in the transition between waggonways and railways and in forms of motive power. Three miles south of Leeds Bridge is an area of long established collieries, now mostly worked out. There are records of mining activity dating back to 1646 and 1669; by 1717 the Brandling family had important interests there.

In more recent years, several separate pits at Middleton, together with Beeston Colliery to the west and Rothwell Haigh to the east, have relied on rail transport, notably the Middleton Railway. They secured an Act of Parliament for their own line as far back as 9 June 1758, specifically a waggonway for the transport of coal. Not that this was the first waggonway in Britain, merely the first authorised by Parliament.

It had progressed from a 3 foot gauge line with wooden rails and a 4 ft gauge with iron rails to a standard 4 ft 8½ in gauge, when, in 1881, it became expedient to have direct connection with the main line railways which had appeared from 1840 onwards. Perhaps the second most important contribution made by the Middleton line to the evolution of railways was its period as the Blenkinsop rack railway of 1812–1834, with locomotives built by Matthew Murray.[1] Relics can now be seen in the National Railway Museum at York and there is a contemporary illustration in the Leeds Mercury of 27 June 1812. The Works of Fenton Murray and Wood were at Holbeck, and Murray was buried in the churchyard there, in 1826.

Acknowledgement was made to Richard Trevithick at the time in respect of his patents, but it is not clear why Blenkinsop's locos were commercially so successful here for over 20 years, presumably on similar primitive track, when Trevithick's own efforts on the Penydarren Trainway were so short lived.

Many changes took place over the succeeding hundred years, culminating with the National Coal Board takeover in 1947 and subsequent withdrawal in 1960.[2] Since then the Middleton Railway Trust Ltd has struggled to maintain in being not only some elements of the old system but also a commercial freight service to private sidings. Indeed, when the M1 motorway was extended northwards into Leeds about 1970, a tunnel was built, in Armco pipe, to carry the old line, and it is the grid reference of this which is given above. Access to it for pedestrians is from the Dewsbury road near the junction with Garnett Road. There is little to be seen now of the original Middleton Railway, but some idea of its historic value is that such efforts have been made to enable a 'railway' well over 200 years old to continue in operation.

7. Stanley Ferry Aqueduct (HEW 191) SE 355 250
Figure 6/1

This is a truly remarkable structure and an Historical Engineering Work of the first order. Unfortunately, like Telford's Menai Suspension Bridge, it is of considerable age and fully used and the strain is beginning to tell. Not only the weight but the size of traffic units have increased considerably since it was built.

It is reckoned to be the largest cast iron aqueduct in the world. It consists of a cast iron trough 165 ft long by 24 ft wide by 8 ft 6 in deep, holding 940 tons of water. This trough is supported by some 35 2¼ in diameter wrought iron hangers at 3 ft centres, each side, from a pair of cast iron segmental arch open web ribs at 30 ft 6 in centres, each in seven segments. The ribs span 155 ft and weigh 110 tons. Each segment is shaped like a five-rung ladder bent to an arc, the T-shaped 'sides' forming the two flanges of the arch ribs which decrease in depth from springing to crown and the 'rungs' being rectangular, part of the web. The abutments are stone, on piles, built by H. McIntosh of London. The castings were by William Graham and Co, Milton Ironworks near Sheffield. The Engineer was George Leather of Leeds.

The aqueduct was built between 1836 and 1839 and opened on 8 August 1839. It carries the new cut of the Aire and Calder Navigation over the River Calder, near Wakefield, and is readily accessible.

8. Brotherton Bridge (HEW 230) SE 482 256
In the early days of main line railways, Robert Stephenson's London and Birmingham Railway was the first link in the route from London to the North. Another link was George Stephenson's North Midland Railway from Derby to Leeds, and its connection

to York from Altofts, near Normanton, the York and North Midland Railway. This passes through Burton Salmon. A short branch was built from there via Ferrybridge (on the Great North Road) to Knottingley where it joined the Wakefield, Pontefract and Goole Railway which ran parallel to the Aire and Calder Navigation. Another branch south from Knottingley to Askern (a few miles north of Doncaster) made it possible for the Great Northern Railway in 1850 to form a new route northward from London (King's Cross). For a time therefore the Knottingley Branch from Burton Salmon became part of the east coast main line and its crossing of the River Aire at Brotherton, close to what is now Ferrybridge Power Station, merited a bridge of some magnitude.

It was in fact similar to the Tubular Bridge at Conwy (HEW 108) and built by J.C. Birkinshaw to the requirements of Robert Stephenson. Birkinshaw had worked with Stephenson on the construction of London and Birmingham Railway.

Brotherton Bridge had twin tubes 250 ft long, 20 ft 6 in high, 11 ft wide separated by 2 ft and with a lead of 25 ft to take care of the skew. The substructure was appropriately monumental, as can be seen today, although altered somewhat when the tubes were replaced in 1901–3 by a pair of 250 ft steel Whipple Murphy trusses at 30 ft 6 in centres, with some 18 underslung cross girders carrying railbearers and longitudinal timbers.

Two plaques record both the original and the present bridges, the latter being designed by W.J. Cudworth and built by the Cleveland Bridge and Engineering Co Ltd of Darlington under the supervision of W.D. Rudgard.

9. Dutch River   (HEW 950)   SE 667 202 to SE 750 228

From Ferrybridge and Brotherton the original Aire and Calder Navigation continued eastward to the Ouse via the River Aire to Airmyn (near the present Boothferry Swing Bridge). This was a difficult section of river to navigate and the Selby Canal cut off was a great improvement. Unfortunately, it had not been made sufficiently wide and deep and a much more ambitious scheme resulted in the Knottingley and Goole Canal of 1826 and the founding of Goole as a port. Telford, Rennie and George Leather were all involved in this, as was Edward Banks of Jolliffe and Banks, the contractors.

There are two swing bridges on the main road through the dock

Figure 6/1. Stanley Ferry Aqueduct (British Waterways Board)

Figure 6/2. Goole Swing Bridge

area in the town of Goole, one of which crosses the Aire and Calder Navigation just before it reaches the Ouse. The one immediately to the south of it is known as Dutch River bridge, and it may also be noted that the adjacent hostelry is called 'The Vermuyden'.

Clearly there is a story behind this, and indeed it does concern Cornelius Vermuyden, the Dutch engineer who is so well remembered for his work on the Bedford Levels in the Fens. Dutch River is actually the outfall of the river Don, an important waterway navigable further upstream from Doncaster at least up to Rotherham. The Don originally had two exits below Thorne, one eastwards, long, flat and meandering via Crowle to Adlingfleet on the Trent, and the other northwards to the Aire which was shorter and straighter.

Just to the south of Thorne are the Levels of Hatfield Chase— territory not unlike the Fens—an area of peat and marsh, tending to be waterlogged and very difficult to drain. Vermuyden signed an agreement with King Charles I in 1626 to turn this waste into good farmland. He did so despite great difficulties and local opposition, with some success, mainly by turning the whole flow of the Don via the northbound channel into the Aire. Unfortunately he misjudged the effect of tides in the Humber, floods in the Aire, Ouse and Trent and the concentrated discharge of the Don on the hitherto untroubled areas below Snaith. The lawsuits which followed forced him to cut a completely new channel to divert the Don away from the Aire to discharge directly to the Ouse at Goole. A sluice was provided but was washed away about 1688 and never replaced. As a navigation canal Dutch River was never very satisfactory, and it was mainly by-passed by other canals early in the 19th century.

10. Goole Swing Bridge (HEW 231) SE 765 247
Figure 6/2

Goole Railway Swing Bridge at Skelton just to the east of the town carries the Doncaster to Hull line over the River Ouse. It is probably the finest example of its kind in the British Isles. Well over a hundred years old, designed and built by some of the foremost engineers and contractors of their day, it is still in full active use.

When opened in 1869 it was said to be the second largest railway swing bridge in the world. It has six sets of three hogback wrought iron plate girders supported on cast iron cylinder piers up to 90 ft in depth to their foundations. There are five fixed spans of 116 ft, one at the east end and four at the west end. The swing span has girders 251 ft long by 16 ft deep and weighs 650 tons. It turns on thirty six 3 ft diameter rollers on a 30 ft diameter race enclosed in a 50 ft diameter pier not unlike a naval gun turret and supported on a cluster of seven cylinders. This leaves two 100 ft openings for navigation.

It was designed by T. E. Harrison and constructed by Butler and Pitts of Stanningley (fixed spans) and W. G. Armstrong and Co of Newcastle upon Tyne (swing span).[3] The bridge was originally operated by hydraulic motors and takes one minute to swing.

11. Water Towers, Goole   (HEW 788 and HEW 921)
SE 741 235   Figure 6/3
Also at Goole, in the town, are two water towers of some note, now in the charge of the Yorkshire Water Authority, South Eastern Division, Doncaster.

The larger tower, of reinforced concrete construction, was the biggest in Europe when built in 1927. The tank is 90 ft in diameter by 22 ft deep with the floor 123 ft above ground level. It is supported on a ring of 24 columns around a 47 ft diameter tower within which are four central columns. The tank capacity is 750 000 gallons. The structure was designed by E.J. Silcock of Leeds and built by H. Arnold and Son of Doncaster.[4]

The smaller brick tower alongside (HEW 921) was built in 1885 to hold 30 000 gallons in a cast iron cylindrical tank 30 ft in diameter. The supporting structure is of good quality red brick in English bond, with a plain cylindrical base and tank surround. The shaft is panelled to give a fluted effect and the tank is roofed by a sheet metal dome. This water tower is now disused but was Listed Grade II in 1978.

12. Selby Swing Bridge, east coast main line railway   (HEW
783)   SE 619 324
In addition to Boothferry swing bridge (1932), Dutch River swing bridge and the railway swing bridge east of Goole, the three swing bridges maintained by the Docks Authority there are South Dock (1899) over the Aire and Calder Navigation, West Dock (1912)

Figure 6/3. Goole water towers

further north in Bridge Street, and Lowther Bridge (1915) near the Lowther Hotel in Aire Street. The hotel is itself of historic interest from its association with the Aire and Calder Navigation.

There are many minor swing bridges over the waterways hereabouts; and two major movable bridges, one at Drax and one at Pollington, disappeared as a result of the railway closures of Dr Beeching. One major example remains, the railway swing bridge at Selby, which, although much smaller and of more recent construction than that near Goole, is for some reason much better known.

Selby railway opening bridge is the second at this site on the River Ouse and it was opened in 1891.[5] Designed under the supervision of Thomas E. Harrison, it was built by Nelson and Co. of York, the ironwork being by the Cleveland Bridge Co., with the swing span machinery by Sir W.G. Armstrong, Mitchell and Co. There are five spans: from the south end, one of 19 ft crosses a road and footpath, another of 15 ft 5 in crosses over a road, then follow a 110 ft 6 in fixed span over the river, the main 130 ft swing span also over the river, and a small 10 ft fixed span over a footpath at the north end. Unlike Goole Bridge there are only two main girders, both tracks being carried on full length cross girders.

The substructure for the main spans is supported on cylinders taken down 78 ft to sandstone. The swing span turns on 24 cast steel rollers of 2 ft 6 in diameter; the cylinder pier is 31 ft in diameter and the main girders 130 ft long, 14 ft 6 in deep (max) at 26 ft centres, with unequal arms of 45 ft and 85 ft necessitating a 92 ton balance weight at the north end.

This bridge replaced an earlier (1839) cast iron two-leaf trunnion bascule bridge [6] giving a 45 ft clear span when open. This was part of the Hull and Selby Railway, whose terminus was alongside the earlier Leeds and Selby Railway terminus, whose buildings still remain at site. Selby only became part of the east coast main line when the old route via Knottingley was shortened by the opening of a Shaftholme–Selby–Chaloner Whin cut-off, known as the York and Doncaster 'branch'.

It is probably its location on the major King's Cross to Edinburgh trunk route rather than its size or age which has made Selby Swing bridge so well known. There are not many places where a small coastal vessel could legitimately bring a 125 mile/h inter city train to a halt while it passed through the temporary gap in the railway. This bridge is just downstream of the Toll Bridge and above the lock to the Selby Canal.

13. Selby station roof   (HEW 518)   SE 618 323
The realignment of tracks through Selby in 1891 for the higher speeds of the new York and Doncaster line swept away the remains of the separate Hull–Selby and Leeds–Selby passenger facilities and produced a new station. There is one engineering feature of interest in it, namely the structural supports to the platform awnings. Cast iron columns at 13 ft centres (cross wise to the track) carry cast iron Vierendeel type girders having four full panels, with two reducing panels at each end for the 8 ft 6 in cantilevers.

Similar roofs exist at Durham (HEW 453) on the main line and at Hexham (HEW 924) on the Newcastle and Carlisle line.

14. Leeds and Selby Railway   (HEW 917)   SE 312 335 to SE 619 323

The period between 1825 and 1835 is much more significant than has yet been fully recognised by railway historians. It began with stationary engines, inclines, horses, slow speed and short length cast iron rails on stone blocks, representing the end of the waggonway era. It ended with locomotives, easy curves and gradients, and speeds hitherto unknown to man, made possible by malleable iron rails five times as long as cast iron rails and by cross sleepers which enabled gauge and cross level to be maintained much more accurately. The dawn of 'real' railways had broken.

It is not surprising that the senior civil engineers of the day saw the need to become involved in this revolutionary form of transport, not only for the opportunity to design and build vast numbers of bridges and earthworks, but also to gain experience in this new concept of tractive power and speed in order to play a prominent part in its development. The Leeds and Selby Railway is almost unknown in books on railway history yet it does occupy a place of some importance from this point of view.

The outlet from the new Selby Coalfield to the British Rail network at Gascoigne Wood (SE 520 317) certainly would have pleased the promoters of the Leeds and Selby Railway. The original intention in 1824 was to build a railway from Leeds to Hull, and George Stephenson was working out a scheme for it while the Stockton and Darlington Railway was being built. At that time the use of inclined planes worked by fixed engines was a distinct possibility.

For various reasons the scheme was shelved and when it was revived in 1829 with James Walker (second President of the Institution from 1835 to 1845) as Engineer, it was for a shorter line to Selby, whence Hull would be served by water transport down the River Ouse. The Leeds and Selby Railway was being planned at the time that *Rocket* was winning the Rainhill Trials competition: it was authorised in 1830 and opened four years later. In a sense it 'missed the boat' since it failed to penetrate to the heart of Leeds and stopped short at Selby instead of going through to Hull, which was not reached until 1840. Walker was without question a first class civil engineer, but perhaps George Stephenson had more of a flair for building railways.

The bridges between Leeds and Gascoigne Wood are notable first for their graceful semi-elliptical shape and second for those over the line being built to take four tracks. There are several of them: that at Garforth (Number 18) (SE 408 335) is easy of access and has an interesting cast iron arched footbridge next to it which is one of the standard North Eastern Railway type (HEW 702).

These elliptical arches are of stone with a span of about 54 ft and were built between 1832 and 1834, that is, soon after the opening of the Liverpool and Manchester Railway and before the London and Birmingham Railway. There is one near South Milford and three between Peckfield Colliery and Garforth. Two more near Cross Gates (Numbers 21 and 23) show that the case for four track provision was strong at the Leeds end. Bridge number 23, now somewhat hidden by road widening, did take four tracks, whereas number 21 on the country side of the station did not. There is also an elliptical arch underbridge (under the railway) at Micklefield (SE 446 327) over the old A1 road, now diverted to the east, and a larger one (number 30 over the Selby Road (A63) at SE 339 340).

As regards buildings, the considerable range remaining at Selby, and illustrated in early books, bear comparison with their contemporaries at Liverpool Road, Manchester.

The Leeds and Selby Railway at Cross Gates passes close to the residence at Austhorpe of the most eminent of all the early civil engineers in this country and the first to describe himself as such— John Smeaton. Smeaton was expected to become a lawyer but his keen interest as a boy in practical construction and mechanisms led to his working in London as a scientific instrument maker. He studied canals and land drainage in Holland and became an expert on water wheels for use in pumping and for driving industrial machinery. He read various scientific papers to the Royal Society and on their recommendation was engaged to build the first successful Eddystone Lighthouse. He was a member of the Society of Civil Engineers—the forerunner (on a rather different basis) of the Institution of Civil Engineers. The Society later took his name and is now known as the Smeatonian Society of Civil Engineers. H. R. H. Prince Philip has honoured it, as he has the Institution, by becoming a member. Smeaton's advice was sought on almost every engineering subject, and his meticulous investigations and specifications, his sound philosophy and the clarity of his reports became a model for all.

15. Richmond Hill Tunnel, Leeds   (HEW 234)
SE 314 334

On a visit for *The Leeds Mercury* of 2 February 1833 a reporter explained that there was not much interest in the construction work because (a) the railway would only run to Selby, not Bradford or Manchester and (b) the Leeds terminus was 'situated at the least agreeable extremity of the town'. Nevertheless even though the original two-track tunnel was enlarged, not duplicated, in the 1890s to take five tracks, which is unusual, and the length is now a mere 118 yd compared with its original 700 yd, this is an Historical Engineering Work.

It was built between 1831 and 1834 by Joseph Nowell of Dewsbury to the requirements of George Smith, Resident Engineer on behalf of Walker and Burges of Westminster. James Walker's ideas 'on ventilating and lighting tunnels' (including this one on the Leeds and Selby Railway) are reported in ref. 7. The three working shafts, about 80 ft deep, had been made permanent by inserting cast iron ellipses 8 ft by 5 ft in the tunnel arch to support 10 ft diameter brick linings.

Tinned copper plate reflectors were installed in an effort to light the tunnel and the walls were whitewashed. Neither this nor the ventilation proved successful, and it was suggested that much larger shafts, perhaps as big as the tunnel itself, might be required.

It is significant that major tunnels such as Kilsby (HEW 55), Box (HEW 236) and Bramhope (HEW 16) do have shafts of greater diameter than the tunnel itself, and it is of interest that James Walker stated in 1836 that he thought his were the first permanent shafts ever built. Richmond Hill was one of the first railway tunnels to be used by locomotives rather than by rope haulage.

16. Bramhope Tunnel   (HEW 16)   SE 242 408 (south) to
SE 256 438 (north)

Bramhope tunnel is 2 miles 241 yd long and has a maximum depth of about 290 ft. It cuts through the ridge separating the Aire and the Wharfe valleys and was built between 1845 and 1849 for the Leeds and Thirsk Railway. This later became the Leeds Northern, then the North Eastern, then the London and North Eastern, and now British Railways.

The Engineer was Thomas Grainger of Edinburgh and the Contractor James Bray of Leeds. It was a difficult job on which 2300 men and 400 horses were employed and 1600 m gal of water had to be pumped out. The strata vary from hard sandstone at the south end, through shales, to clay at the north end, and dip southward: there are seven major faults towards the centre of the bore. The tunnel is on a falling gradient northwards and had at least 34 working faces, namely the two portals, construction shafts 1 to 14, plus two additional shafts at the south end. There may have been three others. Four were made into permanent ventilation shafts of large size, greater than the tunnel itself.

Most of Grainger's work displays very high quality masonry, and the portals at Bramhope are no exception. That at the south end near Horsforth is comparatively plain but in some ways the more striking. The northern portal near Arthington is well known for its two castle-like towers, one large (at one time used as a residence) and one smaller, together with the Company's heraldic device above the tunnel mouth between them. A model of this portal is in Otley Churchyard as a memorial to the men who died during the tunnel construction.

17. Cast iron arch bridge, Newlay and Horsforth   (HEW 189)   SE 239 368

This very attractive bridge carries a minor road over the River Aire in the outskirts of Leeds. It was cast in 1819 by Aydon and Elwell of Shelf Ironworks near Bradford (which firm became part of the Low Moor Ironworks, latterly owned by T.W. Ward). Built as a toll bridge connected with the Micklethwaite Estate, it was taken over in 1888 jointly by the railway (then the Midland Railway) and the Council (Horsforth) and gives access to Newlay and Horsforth Station.

The 82 ft span has four segmental cast iron arch ribs each in three sections, on pin type bearings. The spandrels have plain radials leaving six openings of rhomboid shape in each casting. This is similar to Scarborough Spa Bridge (HEW 211) and the late Dunham Toll Bridge over the Trent (of which there is a model on display at Lincoln). The Newlay Bridge carries a very narrow road of 10 ft width and two nominal 3 ft footways. It was repaired in 1973.

18. 19. Cast iron arch bridges numbers 6 and 8, Thornhill
(HEW 347 and 348)   SE 232 203 and SE 234 205

Rather similar arches with Gothic style sub-arches are used in the spandrels of these two bridges. They were designed by Thomas Grainger and cast by Joseph Butler of Stanningley, Leeds, in 1847.

They carry the ex London and North Western Railway over the Calder and Hebble Navigation and the River Calder respectively. Number 6 is a very skew arch of six ribs, of 100 ft span, 29 ft 4 in width between parapets. Number 8 has two six-rib spans, each of 101 ft by 12 ft rise. Each rib has five segments, 3 ft deep, 12 in top flange, 8 in bottom flange and 2½ in web.

These are two of the oldest cast iron railway underbridges still in full use.

20. North Bridge, Halifax   (HEW 729)   SE 093 257

A much larger cast iron bridge of later vintage (1868–71) replaced the six-arch viaduct of 1774 built to carry the turnpike road over the Hebble Brook at the north end of Halifax. The new bridge, itself by-passed a century later but still in use for local traffic, is a rather magnificent structure in Victorian Gothic style. It has ecclesiastical type buttresses to the stone piers, semi-elliptical arch ribs, perforated with stars, quatrefoils and circles, and two tiers of lancets in the spandrels. The parapets are also decorative but more restrained. There are two main spans of 160 ft with a rise of 16 ft and two approach arches on the town side, and it is 60 ft wide.

The parapet ribs are of cast iron; the six inner ribs spaced 8 ft 7 in apart are partly cast iron with the central 52 ft in wrought iron, a design similar to that used by Thomas Page for Westminster Bridge, London (HEW 264).

Halifax North Bridge was designed by John Fraser of Leeds, and his brother James B. Fraser. John had extensive experience of bridge construction for railways starting with the link line from the original Liverpool and Manchester Railway (HEW 223) into Victoria Station. He was also Resident Engineer under John Hawkshaw during the construction of Lockwood Viaduct (HEW 155).

21. Norfolk Bridge, Sheffield   (HEW 229)   SK 373 892

This elegant cast iron arch is part of the 573 yd 48 span Attercliffe Viaduct which carries the ex-Midland Railway main line over the

Don Valley, a little to the north of Sheffield Midland Station. It was built in 1868–70, which is rather late in the era of cast iron, because the original main line from Derby to Leeds ran direct via Rotherham, by-passing Sheffield.

It has a span of 60 ft square, 80 ft 7½ in skew, and consists of six ribs, each of three segments with a 10 ft rise of arch tapering from 2 ft 6 in to 2 ft 3 in deep surmounted by N-type spandrel bracing and a 7 in timber deck. The cross bracing between the ribs is notable.

22. Abbeydale Industrial Hamlet, Sheffield   (HEW 951)
SK 325 820   Figure 6/4

Two of the most noted ironworks engaged in casting the components for early building and bridge construction were Milton Ironworks near Barnsley and Samuel Walker's at Rotherham. Sheffield, so near to both, has long been famous for quite a different kind of iron and steel, the special quality required for cutting tools and in recent years for armour plate and stainless steel.

One of the reasons for Sheffield's success, apart from the availability of basic materials, was its fast running streams. They were ideal for driving water wheels, the most reliable form of power before the age of steam.

The River Don in Sheffield is joined by the Sheaf and the Rivelin which in turn are fed by Porter Brook and the River Loxley. All these had a succession of weirs and channels leading to water wheels and tail races. Some groups of these look rather like staircase locks on a canal.

The wheels drove all manner of machinery in corn mills, paper mills, snuff mills, rolling mills and forges. More than a dozen of these sites in Sheffield still display their past. Some have just the remnants of walls and buildings; eight of them have their wheels and two or three are more or less in full working order.

Abbeydale is one of these; it has been fully restored and is open daily as one of the Sheffield City Museums. Sited on the A621 Bakewell road, it is a complete unit built for the production of crucible steel and the manufacture of scythes. It comprises a furnace, forge, stores, office, cottages and house. The tilt hammers and other machinery are powered by two backshot and two overshot wheels.

Crucible steel was made in special clay pots charged with about 60 lb of iron and charcoal, melted in the furnace, then lifted and poured ('teemed') into a mould. Abbeydale has a five-hole furnace. This particular process for making high quality steel was introduced by Benjamin Huntsman in the 1740s and was at its peak production in Sheffield between 1860 and 1880.

There is another similar installation a few miles north of Sheffield at Wortley Top Forge (SK 294 998) where both tilt and helve hammers used in the manufacture of railway axles in the 1830s can be seen.

23. Elsecar Colliery Pumping Engine   (HEW 220)
SE 388 000

Water wheels continued to be used as power units until quite recently. They began to be replaced by steam in the mid-18th century, first of all by the Newcomen atmospheric engine. Thomas Newcomen (1663–1729) was a native of Dartmouth and he introduced his engine at Dudley in 1712.[8] In its early form it was called a 'fire engine' and consisted of a haystack boiler below a vertical cylinder. The piston was connected by a chain to a segment on the end of a horizontal rocking beam made of timber. A segment at the other end connected to the pump rods. The segments ensured the verticality of the pump rods, but in later and improved versions this requirement was achieved by James Watt's parallel motion and the rocking beam was made of cast iron.

In an atmospheric engine the steam was not used for direct upward pressure on the piston but for the creation of a vacuum when condensed. This enabled atmospheric pressure to force the piston downward into the cylinder.

The Elsecar engine was installed in 1795 and ran continuously until 1923 (and again in 1931). Its pump lifted over a quarter of a million gallons of water a day from the Barnsley coal seam to an underground drainage level.[9]

A 48 in diameter cylinder replaced the original 42 in diameter one in 1801 and the rocking beam was modernised in 1836 as just described. The original Newcomen design was inefficient in coal consumption but other advantages outweighed this where the fuel was cheap and readily available as at Barnsley.

The Elsecar engine is located in a corner of the National Coal Board depot in a tall building similar to the familiar Cornish

Figure 6/4. Abbeydale Industrial Hamlet (City of Sheffield)

Figure 6/5. Roman road, Blackstone Edge (D.J. Blomley)

engine houses. The cylinder is distinctive; the twin cast iron rocking beams and Watt motion are of the usual type and project outside the building at one end to connect with the long line of wooden pump rods slung between two tall A frames which carry timber beams supporting the linkage bearing.

24. Wicker arches, Sheffield   (HEW 498)   SK 359 881

The Manchester and Sheffield Railway via Woodhead Tunnel was opened in 1845 and extended to Victoria Station four years later. The 41 arches across the Don Valley include a crossing of that well known Sheffield thoroughfare, the Wicker. Despite war damage to the parapet, which has never been properly remedied, and the intrusion of overhead electrification structures, there is probably no finer bridge of its kind on British Railways.

Much of the viaduct is now hidden by buildings and one has the impression of 'Wicker arches' being one main arch flanked by two little ones. As built, however, this was merely the main feature in a viaduct. It was built by Miller, Blackie and Shortridge to the requirements of John Fowler (the Engineer). In view of the important urban location the detailed design was very properly entrusted to a firm of architects, Weightman, Hadfield and Goldie. The result is rather splendid, a four-centred arch of 72 ft span with 30 ft headroom: the voussoirs continue upward across the spandrels to the horizontal moulded course. The side arches of 12 ft span are semi-circular, much lower and surmounted by heraldic decoration. The whole is framed in a rectangular portal and built in good quality ashlar.

25. Woodhead Tunnels   (HEW 235)
SK 114 999 to SE 157 023

Thomas Nicholson was contractor for the first of the three railway tunnels at Standedge but his earlier work at Woodhead is perhaps better known. He constructed the major portion at the eastern end of the first Woodhead Tunnel (1838–45) while Richard Hattersley built the western end. Joseph Locke and Charles Vignoles were both concerned as Engineers. When opened on 22 December 1845 it was, at just over 3 miles, the longest railway tunnel in Britain and although 'beaten' by Standedge only four years later, it was only by a few yards.

A second bore at Woodhead (1847–51) whose contractor was

G. C. Pauling, was anticipated, and provision was made in the first bore for 25 side access connections.

Again, like Standedge, the early work has been superseded by a later double line tunnel, in this case built in 1949–1953, and so far as the original historical engineering work is concerned 'the glory' as it were 'has departed'.

The early tunnels are among the most well known in railway history and have often been described. The modern tunnel is dealt with by Scott and Campbell.[10]

26. Standedge Tunnels   (HEW 12)
SE 007 082 to SE 039 118

Up in the Pennines to the north of Woodhead and south west of Huddersfield the more practicable routes between West Yorkshire and Manchester are blocked by the high ground of Standedge. In the canal era there was a race to close the gap which resulted in three alternative solutions—the long way round to the north (the Leeds and Liverpool Canal), the middle route (extending the Aire and Calder Navigation via the Calder and Hebble by the Rochdale Canal), and the direct route linking Sir John Ramsden's canal at Huddersfield with the Ashton Canal above Manchester (the Huddersfield Canal). This last involved the driving of a canal tunnel which was both the longest (5456 yd) and highest (about 650 ft) above sea level in the United Kingdom.

The Act for it was obtained on 4 April 1794, and the engineer who planned it was Benjamin Outram. It proved to be so difficult and expensive to build that it did not open until 1811. In fact, it took so long that the Rochdale Canal had already been completed before it was available for use, and it was too narrow to be a great success as a rival. The tunnel is on a 4 mile level from Diggle to Marsden, between a rise of about 355 ft in 8¼ miles from the Manchester direction and a descent of about 436 ft in 7½ miles to Huddersfield.

Many vertical shafts were sunk and adits driven during construction. Most did not reach the tunnel itself but served to control the ground water in the upper levels. The tunnel was made 9 ft wide by 17 ft high, with an 8 ft depth of water, something which is difficult to believe nowadays as one's boat grinds on the bottom in the darkness and soot.

Yes—soot, from the railway tunnels. Standedge canal tunnel

proved to be extremely useful in the railway age, and still is. There are three railway tunnels: two single bores, the 'down south' of 1846–49 and the 'up south' of 1868–70, both south of the canal tunnel, and a double track tunnel built in 1890–94 to the north. The last necessitated an extension of the canal tunnel at the Manchester end. Since 1970 this north tunnel has sufficed to carry all traffic and the two single-bore tunnels are now disused. The two earlier tunnels are both 5342 yd long, and until the Severn Tunnel was opened in 1886 were the longest in England.

The railway tunnels have no vertical shafts, only side passages, twelve from the 'down south' to the canal tunnel, and others connecting the railway tunnels with one another. These provide access, ventilation and drainage. The passages were also used to dispose of spoil during construction, debris from the 'down south' being pushed into boats in the canal tunnel.

A unique feature of the tunnels is that there were locomotive pick-up water troughs about 500 yd long on all four tracks within the tunnels themselves. These have, of course, been removed since steam traction was discontinued.

27. March Haigh Dam   (HEW 543)   SE 015 129
The Huddersfield Narrow Canal and Standedge Tunnel both required that water be provided on a large scale near the summit level. Several reservoirs were made, the oldest being at Slaithwaite and the largest, though not actually built until nearly 20 years after the canal opened, at March Haigh, a mile or so north west of the tunnel. The dam is 912 ft long and 60 ft high at the crest.

28. Roman Road, Blackstone Edge   (HEW 916)
SD 966 169   Figure 6/5
Another remarkable road is the stretch of pavement on a gradient of 1 in 5 which crosses the Pennine Way on the 1400 ft contour north of the M62 and south of the A58, on the border of Yorkshire and Lancashire (now West Yorkshire and Greater Manchester).

Some doubt exists about the paving, whether it is Roman, which is probable, or laid in the era of packhorse routes some 1500 years later. The material is local millstone grit which is very durable. The channel shape of the central strip raises more doubts—was it for drainage, for steering or for braking?

There is more certainty about the route. From Manchester (or

Mancunium) an important road ran north east through Oldham, Cleckheaton, Leeds and Tadcaster to York (Eboracum). Another road passed through the sites of Rochdale, Littleborough, up Blackstone Edge, and then swung northward via Luddendenfoot on a direct course to Ilkley (Olicana).

29. Summit Tunnel   (HEW 1003)   SD 940 208 to 946 182
George Stephenson's railway from Manchester to Leeds (actually to Normanton, where it joined the North Midland Railway, linking Derby with Leeds) also took the Littleborough route. Summit Tunnel was built between 1837 and 1840 and is 2885 yd long, the longest railway tunnel in the country at the time of its construction. The impressive south portal is best seen from the adjacent road over the railway.

T. L. Gooch was Stephenson's chief assistant on the Manchester and Leeds project. His brother Daniel Gooch worked on it for a short time before joining the Great Western Railway and achieving fame as its great locomotive engineer.

30. Gauxholme Viaduct near Todmorden   (HEW 2)
SD 931 233
Telford credited the introduction in Great Britain of arched bridge girders supporting the deck system by means of hangers to the Leeds engineer, George Leather. Several road-over-river bridges similar in style to Stanley Ferry Aqueduct (HEW 191) were built in the 1830s. They were often referred to as 'suspension bridges' because the deck was suspended, which is confusing, since the main supporting member was an arch. In a true suspension bridge the deck system hangs from the main members in much the same way, except that the latter are cables or chains in tension and the hangers are made less rigid because of their flexibility. It is this flexibility that has made suspension bridges (unless very large) unsuitable for railways, whereas there are plenty of railway bridge decks suspended from rigid arch members.

George and Robert Stephenson were not slow to adopt the self-contained cast iron arch, so called through having the ends restrained by a wrought iron tie as the bottom chord. The railway tracks were supported by a simple deck system of secondary girders, all hung from the arch.

A whole family of these appeared between 1835 and 1850,

including one in London and another in Derby (since rebuilt), three between Manchester and Leeds, and of course Newcastle High Level Bridge, where the lower deck is suspended and the railway supported. Of the three on the Manchester and Leeds Railway, one has gone, one remains intact but disused at Middleton near Manchester, and one (HEW 2) remains in use. At least its appearance has not altered much from the contemporary pictures of 1840, but it no longer carries the moving load. This is taken by modern girders discreetly hidden behind the facade, in fact, below the cross girders: they are 10 ft deep, 2 ft 6 in flange at 20 ft 9 in centres, and were added in 1906.

The original structure is quite complex. The span is 102 ft and the two girders or trusses are at 32 ft 8 in centres, each arch having a pair of cast iron ribs at 5 ft centres, each tied by four rods forming the effective bottom chord. The arches also have a decorative cast iron bottom chord and an arcade of 34 sub-arches topping the thin columns which shroud the hangers which supported the original cast iron cross girders off the back of the ribs. These arcades are made of almost uniform height throughout and carry a decorative capping which is nearly parallel with the bottom chord. Hence the whole truss looks almost like a parallel flange open web girder.

This metal span across the Rochdale Canal is part of an impressive masonry viaduct built on a curve, sweeping down the valley. It is best seen from the high ground on the side remote from the main road. The railway is part of George Stephenson's Manchester and Leeds route of 1840.

31. Old Hebden Bridge   (HEW 948)   SD 993 274
Roads and habitations tended, in the old days, to keep to the higher ground where it was drier, less wooded, more healthy and generally safer. In the canal era the valleys began to be opened up and the industrial development would be there. A good example of just such a case is at Hebden Bridge, with the older village of Heptonstall above it to the north, connected to Burnley by 'The Long Causeway' on the 1300 ft level.

The lower route from Todmorden to Burnley is however of some age, since the existing stone bridge erected in 1510 is said to have replaced a mediaeval timber bridge. It has three segmental arches of 23 ft span and is 9 ft wide and leads to a steep paved road towards Heptonstall. The bridge has been by-passed and preserved for many years.

32. Kildwick Bridge   (HEW 949)   SE 011 457

Of the many ancient road bridges and pack horse bridges in Yorkshire, perhaps the one at Kildwick on the A629 between Keighley and Skipton is one of the best. John Carr, in the 1752 Book of Bridges (the official record), says this is a very old bridge with ribbed arches of hewn stone and has a 'causey' at the south end. The latter was 220 yd long and the bridge itself 46 yd long.

The two northern arches are pointed and of 18 and 19 ft span. The two main spans over the River Aire are segmental, 29 and 33 ft span. It dates from about 1306 and is a Listed Grade I building. It has been widened on the downstream side and is still in use.

33. Bingley Five-Rise Locks   (HEW 86)   SE 107 398
Figure 6/6

These are not the only staircase locks on British Waterways but they are perhaps the best known and most used. Moreover they are part of a flight of eight—two separate structures fairly close together, one with three steps or rises or locks and the other with five.

The site is at Bingley, north of Leeds, on the Leeds and Liverpool Canal, in a valley which is notable in having a river (the Aire), a road (the A650), a railway (ex-Midland Railway main line) and a canal running parallel and close together.

A minor road, Beck Lane, leads directly to the top lock but, to do full justice to the site, the best approach is probably along the towpath from the car park adjacent to Bingley railway station. This leads first past the three-rise locks, a useful preliminary, as they exhibit most of the features of the five-rise, which are already in view in the middle distance.

Moreover, dwelling on the details of the locks and their gates masks the steepness of the climb. Arrival at the top brings an enhanced reward of the view back down from the greater knowledge of what it contains.

At the top of the five-rise is a small swing bridge and a cluster of houses and buildings, including an early stable block. A plaque on the lock house wall gives the following details:

Open 21 March 1774
Engineer John Longbottom, of Halifax
Built by local stonemasons Barnabas Morvil, Jonathan Farrar, and
Wm Wild, of Bingley and John Sugden, of Wilsden
Rise 59 ft 2 in in 320 ft
16 miles 2 furlongs to Leeds
111 miles to Liverpool

34. Salt's Mill, Saltaire   (HEW 87)   SE 141 381   Figure 6/7

Titus Salt (1803–1876) was one of the great names in the wool industry of the West Riding of Yorkshire.[11] After initial success in Bradford itself, he decided to build a new factory in pleasant surroundings near Shipley. This was only a few miles north of Bradford, and set between the Midland Railway from Leeds to Lancashire and Scotland and the Leeds and Liverpool Canal. Lockwood and Mawson were the architects and William Fairbairn the Engineer.

Salt and Lockwood went to London in 1851 with a view to purchasing some of the buildings used for the Great Exhibition. They did not prove to be suitable for the weight and vibration of the machinery, so a design was worked out for a more solid construction about 500 ft square.

The main block is on the south side, 545 ft long, 50 ft wide and 72 ft high (six storeys, although only four can usually be seen in photographs). It is an attractive building in light stone, not unlike some of the Government buildings in Whitehall. There are long lines of tall square-headed windows, broken by two Italianate towers near the centre, between which is the engine house, and by smaller towers at the extremes. The upper floor, being continuous across the engine house, was reckoned to be the largest room in Europe.

Behind the main building and at right angles, forming a T in plan, is the warehouse, 330 ft long, with a cross piece at the north end. Two- and three-storey extensions of this to east and west mask the main single-storey glass-roofed 330 ft long weaving shed (east side), built for 1200 looms, and the 210 ft by 112 ft combing shed (west side), which lies behind the two-storey office block on the west side of the complex.

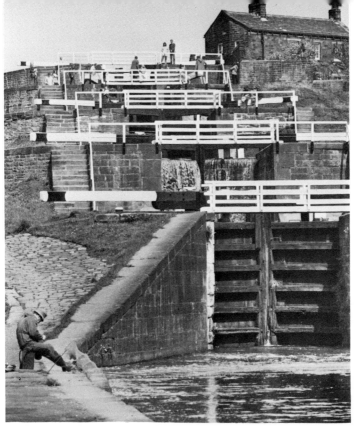

Figure 6/6. Bingley Five-Rise Locks (British Waterways Board)

Figure 6/7. Salt's Mill (Yorkshire Post)

35. Leeds Corn Exchange, domed roof   (HEW 242)
SE 304 334

This roof was built by Butler and Co. of Stanningley to the requirements of Cuthbert Brodrick, the architect who designed Leeds Town Hall and the Grand Hotel at Scarborough. [12]

The Corn Exchange is near the junction of Briggate and Boar Lane, along Duncan Street, and replaced an earlier building in 1867. It is elliptical in plan, 190 ft long by 136 ft wide, with a most impressive domed roof soaring to 75 ft. Its intersecting radial and concentric members create something of the appearance of an inverted basket.

It has nineteen main ribs of semi-elliptical form crossed by semi-circular ribs of light section above and below, with longitudinal boarding above. There is a slated roof and a very large oval roof light.

36. Station buildings, Huddersfield   (HEW 240)
SE 145 168

The Huddersfield and Manchester Railway and Canal Co. was authorised on 21 July 1845. Tenders for the station were accepted on 9 June 1846 and it was partly opened in August 1847, by which time the London and North Western Railway had taken over. The station buildings were completed in October 1850. [13]

They were designed by J.P. Pritchett and Son and the masonry was by the firm of Joseph Kaye. The buildings are 416 ft long, with eight Corinthian columns 68 ft high in the central portion. Heraldic devices are displayed on the wings, and when these are newly painted and the stonework cleaned, Huddersfield station is certainly one of the finest facades in British Rail. Perhaps Monkwearmouth is the nearest equivalent.

Huddersfield was operated jointly by the London and North Western Railway and the Lancashire and Yorkshire Railway from 1849 until they amalgamated in 1922. The building is a splendid expression of Victorian thinking but is no longer appropriate to modern railway operation. It has been taken over by the local authority and forms a worthy part of St George's Square.

37. Lockwood Viaduct, Huddersfield   (HEW 155)
SE 133 146

The Huddersfield and Sheffield Junction Railway was authorised in 1845 to build a short line of 13 miles to connect Huddersfield with Penistone on the Manchester and Sheffield Line. This involved six tunnels and four viaducts, of which the largest is Lockwood.

Designed by John Hawkshaw (later Sir John and one of the most eminent of the Victorian railway engineers, and eleventh President of the Institution) the viaduct was built by Miller Blackie and Shortridge under the watchful eyes of John Fraser (Resident Engineer) and William Bain (Inspector of Works).

It is one of the largest viaducts in the United Kingdom and probably the finest in West Yorkshire. It is 120 ft high and 476 yd long, has 34 semi-circular arches of 30 ft span and two larger spans of 42 ft and 70 ft. It contains nearly a million ft^3 of masonry.[14]

There is a particularly good distant view of it from Beaumont Park but it is most imposing from the public road which passes below it at the south end.

CHAPTER 7

Lancashire and the
Isle of Man

THE names of many of the engineers mentioned in this chapter may not be widely known, though their works are none the less interesting.

Lancashire is very varied in terrain, from moorland in the east to rolling coastal plain in the west. The county is predominantly agricultural, with the manufacturing industries mainly concentrated in towns like Burnley along the river valleys in the south east. Lancaster itself is a relatively small and quiet city set in very pleasant surroundings.

The coastal plain called the Fylde is best known for its seaside holiday resorts. Blackpool is Britain's busiest seaside holiday resort, and its Tower is probably the best known item in this book. The Isle of Man is also a popular holiday area, and is included in this section for that reason.

Perhaps surprisingly, these holiday areas possess many interesting, and in some cases unique, Historical Engineering Works. The 'pursuit of happiness', as enshrined in the American Declaration of Independence, has taxed the minds of many British engineers, and the fruits of some of their labours are described in this section.

1. Blackpool Tower   (HEW 245)   SD 306 360   Figure 7/1

Blackpool Tower took three years to build, and was opened in May 1894. The observation platform at the top is 480 ft above its base, and the height to the top of the flagstaff is 518 ft 9 in. A total of 2493 tons of steel and 93 tons of cast iron form the structure of the Tower, which dwarfs the buildings below, which contain a circus, ballroom, zoo, and other tourist attractions. The Tower was built

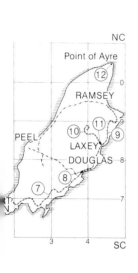

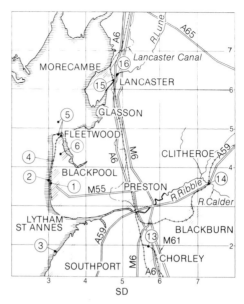

1. Blackpool Tower
2. North Pier, Blackpool
3. Southport Pier
4. Blackpool to Fleetwood Tramway
5. Fleetwood Lighthouses
6. Marsh Mill, Thornton
7. Isle of Man Railway
8. Douglas Bay Tramway, Isle of Man
9. Manx Electric Railway, Isle of Man
10. Snaefell Mountain Railway, Isle of Man
11. Laxey Wheel, Isle of Man
12. Point of Ayre Lighthouse, Isle of Man
13. Flying Arches, Chorley
14. Whalley Viaduct
15. Skerton Bridge, Lancaster
16. Lune Aqueduct, Lancaster

in imitation of the Eiffel Tower, opened in Paris in 1889, and soon proved a popular attraction, despite the fact that it is so much smaller. It was designed by R.J.G. Reade (Engineer) and Maxwell and Tuke (Architects). Heenan and Froude, assisted by James Bell and by R. Neill and Co. were the contractors.[1]

2. North Pier, Blackpool   (HEW 646)   SD 305 364

Blackpool has three piers. This one is the earliest, and the best in the present context. It was designed by Eugenius Birch, the foremost of the Victorian pier designers, built by Laidlaw and Sons of Glasgow, and opened in 1863. The 1070 ft long promenade deck is 28 ft wide, and is supported on plate girders spanning 60 ft between clusters of cast iron columns founded on cast iron screw piles. A 474 ft long jetty for steamers was added in 1867, and the pier head was enlarged for a pavilion, which was opened in 1877. Other alterations have been made since then, and an estimated 12 000 tons of metal were used in its construction.

Central Pier was added in 1868 and South Pier in 1893.[2]

3. Southport Pier (HEW 831)   SD 335 176   Figure 7/2

The pier at Southport is even earlier than that at Blackpool. This was the first true pleasure pier, and it was designed by J. Brunlees and built by W. and J. Galloway. When opened in 1860 at 3600 ft long it was the longest in the country, and it was subsequently extended in 1864 and 1868 to a total of 4380 ft. At the same time the pier was widened and its three rows of piles were increased to four, the new piles being jetted into the sand of the seabed a distance of 15 to 20 ft in an average time of about 25 minutes each.[3] The pier carries modern amusement facilities and a narrow gauge railway, which replaced the original tramway, installed in 1863. Owing to repeated storm damage the length of the pier has been reduced[2] to its present 3650 ft.

4. Blackpool to Fleetwood Tramway   (HEW 631)
SD 305 318 to SD 340 484

Horse trams were introduced into the United Kingdom in 1860 and steam-hauled trams in the late 1870s. In September 1885 the first electric tramway in Britain was opened on Blackpool Promenade. The 2 mile stretch was built by the Blackpool Electric Tramway Co. Ltd in co-operation with Blackpool Corporation, who took over the ownership of the tramway in 1892. Power was supplied through an underground electrical conduit system, the installation of which was supervised by its inventor, M. H. Smith.[4] In 1898 the Blackpool and Fleetwood Tramway Co. Ltd opened a line from Blackpool North Station to the Ferry Terminal in Fleetwood. This new line used overhead electrification, and Blackpool Corporation was quick to see the advantages of this system, and converted their line to the new system by the end of the following year. Various other lines were opened, and by 1920 the Corporation was sole owner of them all.[5] The gradual closure began in 1936 of all except one of the tramway routes, and the route to Marton which closed in 1962 was the last all-street

Figure 7/1. Blackpool Tower and Blackpool–Fleetwood Tramway
(J. Ingham)

tramway in Britain. The remaining 25 track miles run from Starr
Gate at the southern end of Blackpool, 11 miles north to the Ferry
Terminal at Fleetwood, combining both the first two routes that
were once separate. This 4 ft 8½ in gauge tramway is now the only
electric tramway that is still in operation in mainland Britain, and it
maintains a year-round service as well as a tourist service in the
summer season.

Two of the early vehicles are preserved at the Tramway Museum, Crich, Derbyshire.

5. Fleetwood Lighthouses   (HEW 249)
SD 339 484, SD 338 486 and SD 325 513   Figure 7/3

Two onshore lighthouses and an offshore beacon guide ships up the channel of the River Wyre to Fleetwood. They were designed by the architect Decimus Burton FRS and Captain H.M. Denham. The offshore beacon, the Wyre Light, is on a sandbar some 2 miles offshore which is exposed at low tide. The light stands on a platform founded on 3 ft diameter malleable iron screwed piles installed by Mitchell and Son of Belfast,[6] the first time their new piling system was used. It was first lit on 6 June 1840. The two shore lighthouses were first lit on 1 December 1840, originally by gas but now by electricity. The ornate Beach Lighthouse, or Low Light, is three tiered, with square colonnaded base, square shaft, and octagonal top 44 ft above the half tide level, while the slender Pharos Lighthouse or High Light is 104 ft above the half tide level. The offshore beacon platform is carried on seven timber posts, and the shore lighthouses are both built in finely worked sandstone. The lighthouses were built as part of the development of the new town and port of Fleetwood by the Preston and Wyre Railway.[7]

6. Marsh Mill, Thornton   (HEW 617)   SD 335 426
The strong breezes common around Blackpool and the Fylde encouraged the use of windmills. Several survive, of which the best is perhaps that at Thornton. This six-storey brick tower windmill was built in 1794 by Ralph Slater, the best known of the Fylde millwrights. It shows clearly the three distinctive features of Fylde tower windmills—exceptional breadth in proportion to its height; tarred wooden 'cap' in the shape of an up-turned boat; and 'well frame', or 'cap centering' slung beneath the shear beams of the cap to prevent lateral movement of the cap relative to the tower. As originally built, the mill had a 'Lees Flyer' fantail and 'common' sails, though the sails were replaced with 'Cubitt's patent sails' during the last century (Sir William Cubitt being the fifth President of the Institution). The modern replacement sails are built on the basic framework for the patent variety.[8] The mill retains all its original massive wooden machinery, together with several different types of iron governors for the millstones. One of the stones is

Figure 7/2. Southport Pier: sinking the piles

Figure 7/3. Fleetwood Lighthouses: (left) upper light (Pharos); (right) lower light (Beach)

governed using Mead's automatic tentering gear, which was invented seven years before the mill was built. The mill was still in operation during the 1920s, and restoration work started in 1965 has returned the mill to its original working order. Marsh Mill is the only fully preserved Fylde windmill in an area that was once nicknamed 'windmill land'. It is open to the public on certain afternoons in summer, and is a popular tourist attraction.

7. The Isle of Man Railway   (HEW 834)
SC 377 753 to SC 197 689

The Isle of Man is some 30 miles long by 12 miles wide. With the growth in popularity of pleasure steamers in the 1860s, the need for improved land transport for holiday traffic became apparent. The domestic economy also could benefit from the installation of a modest railway system.

The success of the Festiniog Railway in Wales showed the advantages of adopting a track gauge less than the standard 4 ft 8½ in. Fair tonnages of freight and large numbers of passengers could be handled at adequate speeds for the distances involved with tremendous reductions in capital cost for curves, gradients, structures, locomotives and rolling stock.

A gauge of 3 ft, rather larger than that of the Festiniog Railway, was adopted, and despite many financial difficulties, a fairly comprehensive system evolved, covering a large part of the island. There is nothing exceptional in the earthworks and bridgework: that is one of the reasons for adopting a narrow gauge. The passenger stations however, especially that at Douglas, were unusually ambitious.

For those interested in railways, the Isle of Man Railway has great individuality and charm. There is nothing quite like it, now that the narrow gauge systems of Ireland have all gone.

The first section, 11½ miles long, across the island from Douglas to Peel, was opened in 1873. From St Johns, on this route, the Manx Northern Railway, 16½ miles long, running north and north east to Ramsey was added in 1879 and a 3 mile branch south from St Johns to Foxdale in 1886. All these have gone now.

The second line to be opened was the 15 mile Douglas to Castletown and Port Erin (south west and west) line in 1874. This is still in use and being modernised for increased traffic with steam trains.[9]

Figure 7/4. Snaefell Mountain Railway (Manx Electric Railways)

8. Douglas Bay Tramway   (HEW 940)
SC 394 774 to SC 384 745

To the layman this is a mere tourist attraction, something traditional in Douglas. It runs for nearly 2 miles along the promenade from Victoria Pier to Derby Castle, and can therefore be useful as a form of transport if one is not in a great hurry. This 3 ft gauge line was designed and built by Thomas Lightfoot, a retired civil engineering contractor and opened in sections between 1876 and 1902.[10]

It becomes more difficult perhaps as the years roll by to remember that the speed of the horse was universally accepted as normal for transport on land, virtually until 1830. There were fast horses and slow horses, light phaetons and heavy coaches, good roads and bad roads.

For freight transport the development of a satisfactory vehicle/ track relation for maximum load and economy occupied men's thoughts increasingly as the Industrial Revolution progressed. Iron wheels on iron rails was one answer, and for many decades the only answer. Tractive resistance is so low that one horse, literally 1 h.p., could move quite remarkable loads. Moreover the control over direction of movement provided by the track enabled the load to move itself on a falling gradient.

For illustration, and taking a figure at random, the type of 15 ton railway wagon used during the Second World War, having oil lubricated axle boxes, would gravitate from rest on a gradient of 1 in 80 on a 7½ chain radius curve, in winter.

Before the advent of locomotive railways therefore, rail transport with horse traction was common practice, and indeed continued for passenger traffic of a local character until 1914. The Swansea and Mumbles (Oystermouth) Railway had certain similarities to the Douglas Bay Tramway, and a vehicle from the Port Carlisle Railway is in the National Railway Museum at York.

9. Manx Electric Railway, Isle of Man   (HEW 941)
SC 395 774 to SC 452 943
At Derby Castle is the terminus of this railway or tramway, using the bogie car with overhead electric traction. The track gauge is the local standard 3 ft and the 18 miles from Douglas to Ramsey were built in three stages.

The first 2½ miles opened in 1893 and doubled in 1894, largely in connection with a new housing estate. Almost concurrently the line was extended to Laxey. The northern section to Ramsey was added in 1899. There is a connection at Laxey to the Snaefell Mountain Railway. Taken over by the Island Government in 1978, it forms part of a system now being overhauled and modernised.

10. Snaefell Mountain Railway, Isle of Man   (HEW 904)
SC 433 845 to SC 397 879   Figure 7/4
This was the first, and is still the only, electrically worked mountain railway in the British Isles, and was opened on 21 August 1895. The twin tracks rise over 1800 ft in a length of approximately 5 miles, with 85% of the line being on a gradient of 1 in 12. The running rails of Vignoles section, weighing 56 lb/yd are secured to sleepers with fang bolts at a gauge of 3 ft 6 in. A centre rail of the

Figure 7/5. Laxey Wheel (Isle of Man Tourist Board)

type devised by J.B. Fell is incorporated, weighing 65 lb/yd and is bolted to steel chairs set in the centre of the sleepers. The route was surveyed by G. Noble Fell, the track was laid by Mr Herd of Douglas and the electrical equipment installed by Mather and Platt of Manchester. Construction commenced in January 1895, and proceeded so rapidly that the line was opened that August. The six 48-seat passenger cars use overhead pantographs designed by Dr Edward Hopkinson and operate a ten minute interval service, taking only half an hour for the journey in either direction. The Summit Station is 44 ft below the 2034 ft summit of Snaefell Mountain, and the bottom terminus is at Laxey, which is an interchange station with the Manx Electric Railway.

11. Laxey Wheel, Isle of Man   (HEW 397)
SC 432 852   Figure 7/5

'The Lady Isabella' waterwheel was built in 1854 to drain a lead mine. This gigantic structure is the largest waterwheel in the British Isles, being over 72 ft in diameter. It was designed by Robert Casement, a native Manxman, and its 2½ revolutions per minute produce a driving power of 200 h.p. The water that drives the wheel is trapped in a cistern further up the valley. It is brought to the wheel in iron pipes, lifted nearly to the top of the wheel by a syphon, and is then allowed to drop on to wooden buckets attached to the wheel thus causing it to rotate. There are 192 buckets each capable of holding 20 gal of water, and the total weight of the wooden and iron structure is about 100 tons. The wheel used to operate a crank shaft 200 yards long which ran on the top of a row of 35 arches to the mine, where it operated the pumps for dewatering the mine. A spiral staircase of 96 steps now permits visitors to climb to the top of the tower to look down on to the wheel from above.

12. Point of Ayre Lighthouses, Isle of Man   (HEW 936)
NX 464 048

There are several lighthouses of historic interest on the Isle of Man and they are controlled by the Northern Lighthouse Board based in Edinburgh. That on Douglas Head is perhaps the most familiar to visitors, that on Point of Ayre at the north east tip of the island the most accessible and those on Chicken Rock and Calf of Man, at the south west tip, the most interesting and dramatic. The twin lights built there in 1818 by Robert Stevenson were not dissimilar in style from those at Fleetwood. They were abandoned in 1875 when the new light out to sea on Chicken Rock was brought into use but the four-storey upper light is relatively intact. The Act for their construction was sponsored by the Member of Parliament

Figure 7/6. Flying Arches, Chorley

William Huskisson. The modern lighthouse at Calf of Man was added in 1968.

Returning to Point of Ayre, this lighthouse was built to the design of Robert Stevenson, and was first lit on 1 February 1818. It was originally fitted with argand lamps with a 2 ft reflector, but these were replaced by paraffin-fired lamps in 1890 by David Alan Stevenson, the grandson of the original designer. The lighthouse is now fitted with an electric light using a 250W mercury vapour bulb running off mains power, which is visible for up to 30 miles. The iron platform around the top of masonry tower is reached by 107 steps, and a spiral ladder with 17 rungs. The 99 ft tower carries the light 106 ft above high water level. A fog siren tower and a lower lighthouse stand on the foreshore a short distance away from the upper lighthouse. The lower lighthouse was rebuilt in 1950.

13. Flying Arches, Chorley   (HEW 751)   SD 575 195
Figure 7/6

These 16 masonry arches were designed by J. Alexander Adie to strengthen the retaining walls of a railway cutting. They are at 16 ft 6 in centres, span 25 ft 3 in, and have a rise of 3 ft 8 in. In their centres they consist of a single layer of 12 in thick stones topped with stone flags to prevent weathering. They were built in 1841 to strut the retaining walls at either side of the cutting against the anticipated swelling of the clay behind the walls. The cutting is on the Bolton and Preston Railway line, which was opened in 1843, and this form of construction although simple enough in concept is sufficiently rare in application in permanent form as to be worthy of note.[11]

14. Whalley Viaduct   (HEW 566)   SD 728 362

This is the longest and perhaps the most impressive railway viaduct in Lancashire. The 48-span brick arch viaduct was completed in 1850 to carry the Bolton, Blackburn, Clitheroe and West Yorkshire Railway over the valley of the River Calder. The structure is simple in appearance, and its only concession to decoration is on the arch nearest to the remains of Whalley Abbey, where some Gothic treatment has been used to try to harmonise with the remains of the old Abbey. It is a very dominant feature on the local landscape.

15. Skerton Bridge, Lancaster   (HEW 754)   SD 479 624

This classical structure was designed by Thomas Harrison of Chester and was completed in 1788. It carried the main road to Carlisle over the River Lune on five masonry arches each spanning over 60 ft. The level deck of the bridge is 33 ft wide between the parapets, and there are apertures over each pier. An additional span was later built on the southern side over a railway line, though this later span is not in harmony with the rest of the structure.

16. Lune Aqueduct, Lancaster   (HEW 187)   SD 484 638

Architecturally speaking, this is the most outstanding aqueduct in north west England. It carries the Lancaster Canal over the River Lune on five semi-circular arches each of 70 ft span, and the whole structure is over 600 ft long. The abutments at either end are flanked by curved wings, and the structure is faced with rusticated masonry and topped by a stone balustrade. This classical structure has excellent proportions, and it was designed by John Rennie and built by Alexander Stevens and Son. Work on its construction began in January 1794 under the supervision of Archibald Millar. Pozzolana was imported from Italy for the building of the concrete foundations to the piers, and the construction gangs worked double shifts to complete the foundations before the winter set in. The aqueduct was completed in 1796 at a final cost of £48 000.

CHAPTER 8

Merseyside and Greater Manchester

THE modern metropolitan counties of Merseyside and Greater Manchester comprise most of what used to be the industrial belt of south Lancashire, the Wirral peninsula and a former corner of Cheshire. Both counties overlie in part the Lancashire coalfield, which provided the fuel for the heavy industrialisation of this area during the last century.

Greater Manchester is a huge conurbation stretching from towns on the Pennine Moors in the east to the coastal plain in the west. It is dominated by the central industrial cities of Manchester and Salford.

Merseyside is slightly different in character, though still dominated by a major city, Liverpool. Although heavily populated, the coastal plain is also agricultural, and there is pleasant countryside around Southport and on the Wirral peninsula.

Communications have played a vital part in the development of this area. From the start of the Industrial Revolution, raw materials were imported through Liverpool docks in vast quantities, and distributed to mills and factories inland, mostly around the area overlying the coalfield. The finished goods, a large percentage of which were textiles, were then exported via Liverpool again. This intense volume of cargo traffic necessitated good systems of communications, and it is hardly surprising that the first inter-city railway in the world was built to connect Liverpool with Manchester. Rivalry between the two cities led Manchester to build a ship canal at the end of the last century to by-pass the docks at Liverpool.

In discussing the Historical Engineering Works in these two counties it is appropriate to start at the main port of arrival, Liverpool.

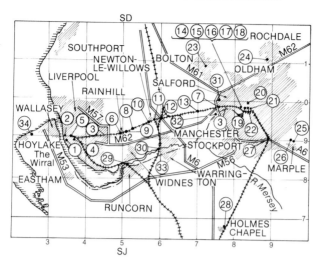

1. Albert Dock Warehouses, Liverpool
2. Royal Liver Building, Liverpool
3. The Liverpool and Manchester
   Railway
4. Wapping and Crown Street
   Tunnels, Liverpool
5. Lime Street Station, Liverpool
6. Skew arch bridge, Rainhill
7. Skew arch bridge, Winton
8. Sutton Bridge
9. Site of the Rainhill Trials
10. Sankey Viaduct
11. Earlestown Station
12. Newton Viaduct
13. Liverpool and Manchester
    Railway over Chat Moss
14. Water Street Bridge, Manchester
15. Water Street cast iron arch bridge,
    Manchester
16. Liverpool Road Station,
    Manchester
17. Old main goods warehouse,

Liverpool Road Station, Manchester
18. Grape Street Warehouse,
    Manchester
19. Deansgate goods warehouse,
    Manchester
20. Victoria Station, Manchester
21. Piccadilly (London Road) Station
    roof, Manchester
22. Manchester Central Station roof
23. Croal Viaduct, Bolton
24. March Barn Bridge, Rochdale
    Canal
25. Marple Aqueduct
26. Brabyns Park Bridge, Marple
27. Stockport Viaduct
28. Dane Viaduct
29. Runcorn Railway Bridge
30. Transporter Bridge, Warrington
31. Bridgewater Canal
32. Barton Aqueduct
33. Manchester Ship Canal
34. Wallasey Embankment

1. Albert Dock Warehouses, Liverpool   (HEW 101)
SJ 362 897   Figure 8/1
The development of Liverpool's dock systems has much in

common with those at Hull. In both cases the mouth of a local
river joining a major waterway not far from the open sea provided
a ready made haven. Simple jetties and quays with the addition of
a graving dock gave place to an enclosed dock and basin. Larger
docks were added to left and right and eventually the original
facilities, completely outmoded, were abandoned and filled in.

The Ler pool or 'Sea Lake' became the Old Dock about 1715,
under the direction of Thomas Steers. It had an entrance basin and
a small dry dock to one side which was enlarged fifteen years later
and became Canning Dock. On the other side, South Dock
appeared about 1750 and was later named Salthouse. George's
Dock and Basin followed on the north side in 1770. South of
Salthouse, Duke's Dock—the virtual terminus of the Bridgewater
Canal—was opened in 1773, and was followed by King's Dock
about 1786 and Queen's in 1796, and then by Brunswick Dock, the
first of Hartley's dock construction in Liverpool.

On the other side, north of George's Dock, Princes, Waterloo,
and Clarence Docks were in use by 1839. By this time the Old
Dock had been filled in and the Customs House built on the site.
Meanwhile, just on the Mersey side of Salthouse Dock the Albert
Dock and warehouses were constructed by Jesse Hartley and Philip
Hardwick and opened by HRH Prince Albert in 1846. They
included the first dockside fireproof warehouses in Liverpool, and
have a resemblance to those at St Katherine's Dock, London. The
concept was monumental in appearance and strength.

The warehouses are constructed of brick, varying from 3 ft to 18
in in thickness; cast iron pillars, 4 ft in diameter and 16 ft high, rise
from the level of the granite quay. The interior structure is in bays
of 19 ft by 12 ft with slim cast iron columns carrying inverted Y-
shaped cast iron beams spanning 19 ft. These take brick jack arches
of 12 ft span with wrought iron tie bars. The supports are founded
partly on granite over sandstone bedrock and partly on beech
friction piles driven into silty sand. The first and second storeys are
12 ft high and the third and fourth storeys are 11 ft high. These
warehouses comprise five five-storey blocks, rising 60 ft to the
galvanised sheet iron roof, on the four sides of the 6¾ acre 650 ft
by 450 ft dock; and were for fifty years used principally in
the handling of cloth, tobacco, wines and spirits. After the
obsolescence of this type of system at the turn of the century,
the warehouses and the vaults below the quay were used for the

bonded storage only of wines, spirits, and tobacco until 1970 (the dock was closed to ships in 1946).

The future of the warehouses has yet to be decided. There was a scheme in 1975 for converting them for use by Liverpool Polytechnic. Proposals have also been made to adapt them for use as a trade centre, or as a maritime museum.[1]

2. Royal Liver Building, Liverpool   (HEW 102)
SJ 338 904

This well known building at Liverpool Pierhead was designed by Walter Aubrey Thomas with the co-operation of L. G. Mouchel and Partners. The contractors were William Brown and Sòns of Salford, for the site, which involved filling in the George's Dock, and Edmund Nuttall and Co. of Trafford Park, Manchester, for the structure. It is not generally realised today that this is not a traditional load bearing masonry but a reinforced concrete structure.

The foundation stone was laid on 11 May 1908 and the building was opened on 19 July 1911. The rapid completion of what was then thought to be the largest reinforced concrete structure in the world was attributed largely to the form of construction. It has nine main floors, two more in the roof structure and six more in the towers.

The building cost £621 000 and originally had nineteen lifts, although there are now only eleven. The principal dimensions are 301 ft by 177 ft by 167 ft (to the main roof) 220 ft (to the clock) and 322 ft to the top of the 18 ft high Liver Birds. The clock is slightly larger than Big Ben. It was set in motion at 1.40 p.m. on 22 June 1911, at the moment King George V was crowned in Westminster Abbey. It was then the largest electric clock in the Commonwealth.[2]

3. The Liverpool and Manchester Railway   (HEW 223)
SJ 345 894 to SJ 833 978

Between Liverpool and Manchester, 31 miles apart, the terrain presents some difficulties. Immediately east of Liverpool is a ridge or plateau of triassic sandstone, followed by another such ridge some 9 miles east of the city. Beyond that, up to 4 miles short of Manchester, peat bogs alternate with southward-flowing tributaries of the River Mersey. The first (1824) project for a main-line railway linking the two cities was for a northerly route which almost avoided the ridges, but the Bill to authorise it was rejected by the House of Lords.

In 1826 Parliament sanctioned a bolder and more direct route passing through the first ridge by tunnels and deep rock cuttings and rising over the second by inclines intended to be worked by stationary engines. From the Liverpool terminus at Wapping, near Queen's Dock, it started with a double-line tunnel, rising at a gradient of about 1 in 48 (2.08%) to a 40 ft deep rock cutting in Edge Hill, where stationary engines were located for hauling goods wagons through the tunnel. The western end of this cutting was a tunnel headwall with the double-line opening of the Wapping Tunnel (item 4) in the centre, flanked by a single-line tunnel (too small for locomotives) on the right, leading to the first passenger station at Crown Street, and by a matching blind arch on the left which was later carried through to Crown Street coal yard but as a double-line tunnel authorised by the Liverpool and Manchester Railway Act of 1845.

The rock cutting at Edge Hill, to which the two stationary-engine houses linked by a 'Moorish' arch across the double line of railway gave a monumental aspect, was the western terminus of locomotive-engine haulage. Thence eastwards, the line proceeded at easy gradients for 5¾ miles, traversing the imposing cutting, 70 ft deep with almost vertical rock sides, through Olive Mount, followed by a long embankment formed with the spoil from the cutting.

To cross the second ridge, the line ascended the 1½ mile long Whiston Inclined Plane at an average gradient of 1 in 96 (1.04%). Nearly 2 miles of almost level track, the Rainhill Level, separated it from the top of the Sutton Inclined Plane, of similar length and gradient. It was this Level which was used for the locomotive trials in October 1829, when the success of Robert Stephenson's *Rocket* (see item 9) not only demonstrated the superiority of steam traction over horse traction but also showed that rope haulage was not needed on the Whiston and Sutton Inclines.

The first of the peat bogs, Parr Moss, lay just beyond the foot of the Sutton Incline: some 20 ft deep to the underlying clay, it needed 25 ft of rock and clay from the cutting on the Sutton Incline to form an embankment 5 ft high. More challenging was the 4¾ mile long embankment across Chat Moss, which took 3½ years to conquer (HEW 952).

In traversing the better-drained land between Parr Moss and Chat Moss the line crosses the valley of the Sankey Brook (in which was one of the earliest canals, the St Helens Canal) by a viaduct of nine arches (see item 10). One and a half miles farther east it passes over the four-arch Newton Viaduct. This is followed by a long cutting, at the centre of which is the short Kenyon Tunnel, and by the Broseley Embankment, formed with spoil from the Kenyon Cutting and extending to the Glaze Brook, which forms the westerly boundary of Chat Moss and is crossed by a 30 ft brick arch.

East of Chat Moss, the railway passes through Eccles and Salford, mainly in shallow cutting. At the Manchester end, the original (1826) authorisation provided for a terminus at the New Bailey in Salford, but the amending Act of 1829 diverted the railway to a terminus within Manchester at the corner of Liverpool Road and Water Street (HEW 100). To enter Manchester it crossed the River Irwell by a stone arched bridge with two 66 ft skew spans.

Overline bridges were generally brick or stone arches of 30 ft square span. The most notable skew overbridge is that at Rainhill (item 6). Underline bridges were most commonly stone arches of 12 ft span, but some, over public roads, were somewhat wider, the widest being Winton Skew Bridge, near Patricroft, of 20 ft square span and 31 ft skew span. Of the 64 original bridges, some part of 37 still survives, but nearly all have been modified to some extent by widenings of the railway or of roads. There were many level crossings, mostly later converted to bridges; some of the crossings (gates) gave their names to rudimentary intermediate halts, many of which later became stations.

The Engineer for the 1824 project was George Stephenson, but being a blunt practical man he was at a disadvantage when giving evidence in Parliament, so the promoters called in the Rennies to take responsibility for the 1825-6 survey, the work being done mainly by Charles Vignoles. Stephenson was then re-engaged as Engineer in charge of construction. The work was split up into a large number of contracts, of which the principal ones are listed below, and some of it appears to have been done by direct labour under Stephenson's direction.

The contractors for the Wapping Tunnel were Copeland,

Stevenson and Harding. Work began from the two ends and from intermediate shafts early in 1827, and by mid-June 1828 the headings had met. The tunnel was completed by the end of 1828 despite a fall of roof under Crown Street. Thornton and Co undertook excavation east of the tunnel and J. and G. Stevenson that of the Olive Mount Cutting. The Whiston Cutting was excavated by M'Cloud and Alcock, that at Rainhill by Copeland, Pickering and Co, and that at Sutton by Eaton. The Sankey Embankment was formed by Greenshields, that at Newton by Baird and Hutchinson and that at Broseley by Blacklock. The Chat Moss Embankment was undertaken by Blacklock, Willy and others. For the Salford Cutting the contractor was Stannard. The total cost of the fixed works was about £820 000. The original track was of 35 lb/yd T-shaped malleable iron rails 15 ft long, fish-bellied between supports 3 ft apart. Where the formation was firm the supporting chairs were carried on large stone 'pot' sleepers and on the 13 miles of embankments by oak sleepers. The rails were soon found to be too light, and successively heavier sections were introduced.

The formal opening of the railway was on 15 September 1830, a day marred by a fatal accident at Parkside Station to the Member of Parliament for Liverpool and former President of the Board of Trade, William Huskisson. There is a lineside monument to him at the site, SJ 605 955. The whole line was opened to the public for traffic on the following day.

The Crown Street terminus (just outside the then Liverpool boundary) proving inconvenient, the Liverpool and Manchester Company constructed a branch, authorised in 1832 and opened on 15 August 1836, from Edge Hill Junction (east of the original engine station and of the present Edge Hill Station) to a new passenger station at Lime Street, the first of three on that site (item 5). The present Edge Hill passenger station is on the 1836 Lime Street Branch, which was originally in tunnel between the two stations, at a gradient of about 1 in 90 (1.11%), operated by rope haulage until about 1870. In the 1870s, when the line was quadrupled, most of the tunnel was opened out. At the Manchester end, prolonged controversy about linkage with other railways culminated in the opening by the Liverpool and Manchester Railway Company of a sinuous link to the Manchester and Leeds Railway at Victoria Station (the present Platform 11

Figure 8/1. Albert Dock warehouses (Building Design Partnership)

Figure 8/2. Rainhill skew arch bridge (British Rail)

there) in 1844, followed in 1849 by the Manchester South Junction
and Altrincham joint line, wholly on viaduct and including the still
existing cast-iron arch over Water Street (item 15).

The Liverpool and Manchester Railway Company was absorbed
by the Grand Junction Railway Company by the latter Company's
Act of 8 August 1845. The Company's last Act, only eleven days
earlier, authorised branches including one to the Waterloo Dock at
Liverpool, through a third steeply graded tunnel radiating from
Edge Hill and worked initially by rope haulage; it was opened for
goods traffic in 1849 and to Riverside Station for passengers to and
from ocean liners in 1895.[2-4]

So great was interest in the line that a set of commemorative
engravings was issued to mark the achievement. Initially seven
drawings were issued early in 1831. They were 10 in x 8 in in size,
drawn by T.T. Bury, engraved by H. Pyall and published by R.
Ackermann. Six more were added in July 1831 and a fourteenth in
1832. They were:

(1)   The tunnel, that is, Wapping, long since disused (HEW
       953).
(2)   Entrance to railway at Edge Hill; actually of the three
       tunnel portals and two chimneys at the west end of a deep
       excavation in the rock known as the stationary engine area.
       This was the end of the cable worked inclines from
       Crown Street and Wapping and the commencement of the
       locomotive-worked Liverpool and Manchester Railway
       proper (see item 10)
(3)   Olive Mount Cutting. A prodigious feat of excavation, still
       there in use but no longer so dramatic in appearance
       because of subsequent railway widenings.
(4)   Sankey Viaduct, still in use (HEW 94).
(5)   Chat Moss, somewhat tamed now but still to be seen
       (HEW 952).
(6)   Water Street Bridge, reconstructed about 1908 (HEW 911).
(7)   Rolling Stock.
(8)   Railway Offices, Liverpool. This was Crown Street, of
       which nothing remains now.
(9)   Warehouses at Wapping. Little remains now but note the
       tunnel portal with two-track cable haulage.
(10)   Moorish Arch. This was at the east end of the motive

power exchange point mentioned in (2) above. Little remains of it now.

(11) View near Liverpool, changed by widenings.

(12) Rainhill Bridge, still in use (HEW 553)

(13) Parkside Station. Clearly the important stage for watering locomotives. Little to be seen now except the memorial to William Huskisson.

(14) Intersection Bridge. A two span cast iron beam bridge added after the Liverpool and Manchester Railway opening to carry another line. So many changes have been made over the years that very little of the original structure remains.

4. Wapping and Crown Street Tunnels   (HEW 953)
SJ 345 894 to SJ 369 893

All three major 'firsts' in the history of locomotive railways—the Stockton and Darlington (1825), the Liverpool and Manchester (1830) and the London and Birmingham (1835) Railways incorporated cable worked inclines.

The first (Etherley and Brusselton) and the last (Euston and Camden) were in the open. The Liverpool and Manchester Railway inclines were in tunnels, initially two (Wapping and Crown Street) and eventually four (Lime Street, 1836, and Waterloo, 1849) and the practice persisted as late as 1895.

Between the docks area of Liverpool and the present Edge Hill Station the ground rises well over 100 ft. Because the area was already built up, the new railways had to cover this length in a tunnel. Passengers bound for Manchester therefore started their journey faced with two hazards, first the frightening experience of negotiating an underground passage, and second the uncertainty that the journey had really begun until brief hiatus near the Moorish arch was followed by a fresh start behind a real locomotive.

The single track Crown Street Tunnel was only 291 yd long, 15 ft wide and 12 ft high, too small for locomotives and not very impressive. The track gradient was in fact falling towards Edge Hill, so departing trains could proceed by gravity to the place where they would acquire a locomotive. It was built in 1829 and still exists complete with the original portals. Passenger services through it ceased in 1836.

From the same eastern end, the much longer Wapping Tunnel (2111 yd) passes slightly to the south, with a ventilation shaft actually in Crown Street Yard. For 1980 yd it falls on the steep gradient of 1 in 48 flattening out as it reaches 300 yd at the west end. Compared with earlier tunnels, such as for canals or for drainage works, its cross section of 22 ft by 16 ft high was very large, and this made quite an impression at the time. It was built between 1826 and 1828 and was officially opened in July 1829 with double track and rope haulage. The walls were whitewashed and gas lighting installed, and for some time it was a tourist attraction open to the public for inspection.

Locomotive working replaced the cables in May 1896 and lasted until 1965 when the goods yard (Park Lane) which it served was closed and the tunnel was no longer required.

Charles Vignoles, George Stephenson, T.L. Gooch, and Joseph Locke were all concerned at one time or another with the survey, setting out and construction. Vignoles's survey on behalf of the Rennies was the basis for the second and successful approach to Parliament for authority to build the Liverpool and Manchester Railway and it included this tunnel.

Vignoles was retained to set out the line but for reasons outside his control the appointment was unacceptable to George Stephenson. Stephenson complained in November 1826 that the pilot heading near the first shaft was 4 yd off course and that the foundations of certain houses would be at risk, and in other ways his attitude soon forced Vignoles to resign.

Joseph Locke took over and the tunnel was eventually completed satisfactorily. It has a nearly semi-circular arch and straight side walls all in brick. During its brief period as a showpiece the names of the streets above it were displayed on the side walls.

In retrospect, the importance of Wapping and Crown Street Tunnels in the history of railways has been overlooked for too long, and the quality of what remains does merit restoration and inclusion in a Heritage Trail.

A second tunnel into Crown Street was made by enlarging the third hole in the original east portal and continuing the bore at a size appropriate to locomotive working. The fourth tunnel was built in 1836 to serve the new terminus at Lime Street, which is well to the north of the old Liverpool and Manchester Railway terminus; it was 2025 yd long on a gradient of 1 in 97 and traffic was rope-worked until 1870. The tunnel was altered more than once and eventually opened out. The fifth tunnel is from the present Edge Hill station to the Victoria and Waterloo Docks. It was opened in 1849 and passes to the north of Lime Street Station; it consists of the Victoria Tunnel 2707 yd to the east and the Waterloo Tunnel 850 yd to the west. It was rope-worked until 1895, when passenger services to Riverside Station commenced; but these ceased in 1971, and the tunnel itself was disused not long after.

5. Lime Street Station, Liverpool   (HEW 103)   SJ 351 906

As the centre of urban activity moved about 1770 from Ler pool (which became the Old Dock) to George's Dock and Basin, now the site of Pierhead, development inland from there focussed on St George's Hall. Clearly, a site for the new railway station, so badly needed to replace the outdated Crown Street, had to be in this vicinity. Lime Street Station was opened in August 1836 and the imposing facade with four main arched openings is included among Ackermann's engravings.

The earliest roof had timber trusses on cast iron columns and arcades. This was replaced about twelve years later by a single 153 ft 6 in span iron roof with curved trusses over six tracks, three platforms and a roadway.[6]

At this time the site was very restricted, but in 1865 the whole station was lengthened (towards Manchester) and widened and the first of the two existing roofs was provided, approximately 600 ft long and 200 ft span (the dimensions vary down the site, which is both curved and tapering, from 215 ft to 185 ft).

The second span followed in 1875 and tapers from 195 ft to 170 ft. Both are distinctive in type with trusses supported on masonry walls on both sides and on twin cast iron columns down the middle.

Both top and bottom main members of the trusses are curved with intervening bracing of the Warren girder type. Walmisley quotes a 44 ft 9 in total height of truss made up of 22 ft rise of bottom tie and 22 ft 9 in depth. They are at 32 ft centres. The top rib is of built-up I-section 12 in by 15 in and the lower rib of four 6 in by 1 in flats. The web members are built up barrel shaped, and the purlins open web, parallel chord, girders.

Birmingham New Street used to have a roof of this type before the station was completely rebuilt and modernised.

6. Skew Arch Bridge, Rainhill   (HEW 553)   SJ 490 914
Figure 8/2

The Rainhill skew arch bridge carries the old turnpike road of 1753, now the A57 between Liverpool and Manchester, over the first railway linking the two towns.

The bridge passes over the railway at an angle of 34°, with a skew span of 54 ft (30 ft on square). It was constructed of masonry at a cost of £3735, the stone being obtained from a local quarry. The individual stones are a very odd shape due to the combination of arch and skew. Legend has it that to enable the masons to select and cut the voussoirs correctly before erection, a wooden model (possibly full size) was made and cut up as necessary along the course lines: some say the material used was not wood but cheese. Again the fame of Rainhill bridge is such that it is assumed to be unique, whereas Booth's schedule shows it to be one of sixteen skew bridges on the Liverpool and Manchester Railway, although it is certainly the most notable.

7. Skew Arch Bridge, Winton   (HEW 954)   SJ 760 987
Possibly Winton is the best remaining example of a skew arch built to carry the railway. Winton Bridge has a 31 ft skew span, 20 ft on the square.

8. Sutton Bridge   (HEW 945)   SJ 522 926
Sutton Bridge is 'New Street', Marshalls Cross. This has a 30 ft square span and an almost semi-circular arch, with voussoirs as at Rainhill continued radially up to the horizontal string course. It carries road over rail and would seem to be one of the best surviving of the early bridges.

9. Site of the Rainhill Trials   (HEW 944)
SJ 482 913 to SJ 510 920   Figure 8/3

Construction of the Liverpool and Manchester Railway was well advanced before a decision was reached on the form of motive power to work the traffic. Horse traction could not be discounted; it was still widely used everywhere and was at least reliable. Winding engines and rope haulage were generally well developed and understood and readily obtainable. There was no question about their efficacy for inclines but could they be applied to a 30 mile mainly level railway? One scheme was worked out for dividing the Liverpool and Manchester Railway into sections of about 1½ miles and using 21 fixed engines.

Stephenson himself recommended three fixed engines, one for Wapping Tunnel (which was built) and two for Whiston and Sutton, at either end of the Rainhill level. He also had vast experience with locomotives and great confidence in them, not only as they were at that date, but in the very rapid development which he felt sure would result once they became more widely used.

Several Liverpool and Manchester Railway deputations were sent to inspect the newly opened Stockton and Darlington Railway and the many other places where locomotives were already being used with more or less success. There were nearly 30 in Yorkshire, Durham and Northumberland, more than half of them built by George Stephenson. Eminent civil engineers of the day were engaged to inspect and report and their view was that fixed engines were currently more reliable although locomotives had perhaps the most future potential.

It was decided to offer a prize for the best locomotive to comply with six set conditions over a 1½ mile course at Rainhill in October 1829. The judges were J. U. Rastrick, Nicholas Wood and John Kennedy, and there were five entries. The contest was really between the only three teams in the country, and perhaps in the world, at that time capable of success—Ericsson and Braithwaite of London with a background of steam-driven road vehicles, Timothy Hackworth of Shildon, just then in the lead with improved boiler design and George Stephenson, representing the Forth Street (or South Street) Works in Newcastle.

Stephenson had a wealth of personal experience of the hard practical kind, not brilliant untried experiment. There were only two reasons why he might not succeed. First, he had recently become primarily a builder of railways instead of locomotives, and second, his conduct of affairs was basically dependent on test results. He had less trust in theory; even scale drawings were to him more useful for recording results than for planning ahead.

Nevertheless his locomotives were more numerous and more successful than any others and he was aware of his personal weakness which was due to a lack of formal education. He relied on his son Robert to make up for the deficiency and Robert's long absence in South America from 1824 to 1827 put an enormous strain on the ability of the Forth Street Works to progress or even to meet its commitments.

Soon after Robert Stephenson returned, a competent draughtsman was engaged and various sound ideas already in mind were rapidly developed and augmented. The teamwork was irresistible: Robert could hardly go wrong with a man like George behind him.

In 1829 *Lancashire Witch* was supplied to the Bolton and Leigh Railway, incorporating four innovations, three of which proved their worth and were built into the *Rocket*, the fourth (expansive working) being dropped as a little premature and hence unreliable.

Robert's most personal contribution to the *Rocket* was the multi-tube boiler, already on the way, but untested and therefore a calculated risk which in the event paid off. He also had to work very hard to achieve sufficient technical perfection with it in the time available.

Of the designers of the three locomotives which did compete at Rainhill only Stephenson had fully appreciated the real needs underlying the Liverpool and Manchester Railway specification, one of which was speed. For that reason the four wheels were not coupled: the driving wheels were 4 ft 8 in diameter and the trailing wheels 2 ft 6 in diameter. The wheels were sprung and the cylinders inclined, to reduce damage to the permanent way. The *Rocket* itself was 12 ft 6 in long and 15 ft high to the top of the chimney. The tender was a mere appendage, not even built by the Stephensons.

The winning feature was the efficiency of the boiler. It was 6 ft long by 3 ft 4 in diameter and contained 25 copper tubes 3 in diameter in the lower half and a small dome to ensure dry steam in the upper half. The tubes were fitted to a water jacketed firebox 2 ft wide by 3 ft high and pointed at the chimney end to assist the draught already ensured by the two 1½ in diameter exhaust steam blast pipes. Steam pressure was 50 lb/in^2.

Rocket was tried out at Killingworth, dismantled and sent by road to Carlisle, thence by canal to Bowness and ship to Liverpool. It had no difficulty in meeting all the requirements of the trial and its final run at 35 mile/h was quite sensational.

Rocket won easily, but that did not exhaust the Stephensons. A

Figure 8/3. Rocket (replica) (Science Museum)

Figure 8/4. Water Street Bridge (Ackermann)

much improved version *Northumbrian* was already on the way and delivered before the Liverpool and Manchester Railway opening in September 1830. Yet another locomotive, *Planet*, a revolutionary advance on both, arrived only a few weeks later.

When *Rocket* became obsolete, despite alterations such as making the cylinders more nearly horizontal, it was in 1839 sold to a colliery railway near Carlisle. After 12 years it returned to the Forth Street Works, where it was built, and it was later presented to the Patent Museum. It is now in the Science Museum, together with a replica there showing *Rocket* as it was originally at the time of the Rainhill trials.

10. Sankey Viaduct   (HEW 94)   SJ 569 948

This is probably the first viaduct of any size in the railway era and no doubt owes something of its design to the earlier canal aqueducts. It was commenced in 1828, and opened in September 1830. Its nine semi-circular arches, each of 50 ft span, carry the railway over the Sankey Brook at a height of 70 ft. The viaduct is built of brick with stone facings. Each of its piers rests on approximately 200 timber piles, which vary in length from 20 to 30 ft. The viaduct has a particularly sturdy appearance, due to the wide splay to the pier bases, but the slender pilasters extending from them up to the parapets add a graceful touch. The viaduct is listed as a structure of historical and architectural interest.

11. Earlestown Station   (HEW 946)   SJ 578 951

A branch line to Warrington was authorised in 1829, engineered by Robert Stephenson and opened in 1831. Its junction with the Liverpool and Manchester Railway was called Newton Junction and, from 1861, Earlestown. When the Grand Junction Railway was opened from Birmingham the branch became part of the main line from Euston to Liverpool, and an east curve was added in 1837 to serve Manchester. Vulcan Foundry, one of the famous locomotive building firms, was located on the branch, and the London and North Western Railway set up a wagon works at Earlestown.

On the island platform at the station is a Tudor-style waiting room of some architectural merit, built probably in the early 1840s. There is an unusual and rather attractive platform awning.

12. Newton Viaduct   (HEW 932)   SJ 593 953

Although somewhat overshadowed by its more illustrious neighbour Sankey Viaduct, the present bridge at Newton le Willows is quite an attractive structure. It is of red brick with stone voussoirs and pilasters and has four semi-circular arches of 30 ft span and is 40 ft high.

13. Liverpool and Manchester Railway over Chat Moss
(HEW 952)   SJ 704 973

One of the engineering achievements of the Liverpool and Manchester Railway was the conquest of Chat Moss. This is an area about 5 miles long on the line of the railway consisting of a glacial depression or basin ranging from 15 ft to 36 ft deep, filled with waterlogged vegetable matter. It is more than filled, since the surface resembles a shallow dome.

The upper layers consist of mosses, grasses and heather, decaying into peat. At the base, the Moss contains the remains of larch, birch and other small trees. Drainage is not easy, as the bog will be 90–93% water by volume. It is often difficult if not impossible for a man or a horse to stand on it: ditches tend to close up from sheer instability: if they do remain, the flow gradient to them is very steep, so that they are not effective for any great distance.

Any suggestion in 1826 to build a railway across such ground met with scepticism and ridicule, but George Stephenson was convinced that it could be done. Certainly the technique which he adopted—spreading the load over a wide base—had been used before.

Unstable ground like Chat Moss was nothing new to engineers experienced in Holland or the East Anglian Fens; Metcalfe had used bundles of heather below the base of his road past Pule Hill: reclamation for agricultural purposes on a small scale had been going on for a decade on Chat Moss itself. Local men, Roscoe and Stannard, were using narrow gauge waggonways floated on 'mattresses' of brushwood already.

Whether these methods could be applied successfully to a full size railway was another matter. George Stephenson thought that they could, and for the most part, apart from the obvious difficulties, all went quite well. In some parts however they did not, especially towards the east end, and there were times in 1827 when progress became nil and even negative. Vast amounts of material were tipped and spread but simply disappeared.

The two side ditches 48 ft apart kept closing up. Old tar barrels were used to make wooden culverts. The nearby Botany Bay Wood was purchased to supply small trees, branches and twigs to make hurdles and mattresses. Dried peat, turves, brushwood, heather, earth and cinders eventually did the trick, and on 1 January 1830 a track was laid and *Rocket* passed over it with a trial train.

It is interesting to compare this with the recent (1974) experience of building the M62 motorway across the south area of Chat Moss and actually under the Liverpool and Manchester Railway at its eastern boundary. There are great differences. It was possible to sink the M62 some 20–30 ft below ground and found it directly on the firmer stratum. Stephenson did his work by hand, while almost unlimited mechanical plant was available on the M62. Something like a milion yd³ of peat was actually removed. Huge ditches like miniature cuttings were dug on either side of the motorway alignment and immediately filled with slag. These formed buttresses to hold back the peat outside when the centre part of the permanent cutting was dug out, including two thirds of the slag.

Astley Signal Box is near the centre and the deepest part of the moss and is easily accessible. A good impression of the conditions can be obtained by standing there and feeling the ground tremble at the passage of a train.

14. Water Street Bridge, Manchester   (HEW 911)
SJ 829 979   Figure 8/4

The original bridge across Water Street led to what is widely regarded as the oldest railway station in the world and the bridge itself is widely known from the Bury/Ackermann coloured engraving. Had it survived until today instead of being ignominiously destroyed to achieve a local road improvement, it might well have ranked next to Ironbridge, Coalbrookdale. The present bridge dates from 1908 and is a very ordinary steel plate girder bridge of modest span. The original bridge, completed in 1830, was almost certainly the first iron beam bridge, as distinct from an arch or a truss, to carry a railway using locomotives.

Both the flat soffit design and the solid iron parapets seem to have been dictated by the Manchester Civic authorities. The architectural design emulating a Greek temple was more exotic than the passenger station itself. Structurally the two footways were in arched subways of masonry under-drawn by flat slabs. The nine fluted columns forming each pier were mostly if not wholly of stone; photographs taken shortly before the bridge was replaced show the end column still fluted but the interior ones plain.

The iron bridge—the pioneer use of H-section cast iron beams—was basically a clear span of 26 ft. There were three main beams 27½ in deep, 16 in by 3 in bottom flange, 4 in top flange, (the 16 in being at the centre since the flange was parabolic in plan) with smaller cross beams at 3 ft centres and brick jack arches. The two face beams were also main beams, of similar section to the other three, but arranged eccentrically so as to present a small flange projection to the outside and a large one inside, to support not only the cross girders but also the parapet standards.

Fairbairn and Lillie were the contractors; William Fairbairn (1789–1874) almost certainly designed the superstructure, no doubt submitting his detailed proposals for searching criticism by George Stephenson (1781–1848) who was not only the Liverpool and Manchester Railway engineer but also an old friend of Fairbairn. They would both have had a sound and healthy respect for each other's judgement and abilities.

Fairbairn was interested in the design and construction of cotton mills and their machinery. The best distribution of material in a cast iron beam section was being widely debated at that time, and Fairbairn was quick to realise the genius of the mathematician, Eaton Hodgkinson (1789–1861) and to assist him in putting his particular theories to the test with small models tested to destruction. The form of beam sections advocated by Hodgkinson was used for Water Street and was soon adopted by the engineering profession generally. Nearly 20 years later Fairbairn and Hodgkinson collaborated with Robert Stephenson in the design, testing and construction of wrought iron tubular girders for Britannia Bridge on the Chester and Holyhead Railway.

15. Water Street cast iron arch bridge   (HEW 753)
SJ 829 979
The need for a beam bridge having a flat soffit seems to have disappeared by the time the adjacent Manchester South Junction and Altrincham Railway was carried across Water Street.

Opened in 1848, this bridge has two railway tracks carried by six cast iron arch ribs, each cast in three sections, butted and bolted together. The span is about 50 ft and the bridge is on a slight skew.

The ribs are dumb bell section 6¾ in wide by 2 ft 3 in deep at the springing reducing to 1 ft 10½ in at the crown, with a rise of 7 ft. The spandrel bracing is of the X pattern, cruciform section, and there are panelled and decorated cast iron parapets. The sleepered track and ballast are carried on cast iron floorplates.

16. Liverpool Road Station   (HEW 100)   SJ 830 979
Figure 8/5

The railway between Ordsall Lane and the first Manchester terminus at Liverpool Road was authorised by the Liverpool and Manchester Railway Act, 1829, as a deviation from the route authorised in 1826, which would have terminated in Salford. The terminus was approached by a stone bridge over the River Irwell, with two arches of a skew span of 66 ft and a square span of 64 ft 6 in. It was 53 ft wide between parapets, accommodating not only a double line of railway but also a road 18 ft wide for the use of the Mersey and Irwell Navigation.

East of the river the railway is carried on a series of brick arches and then crosses Water Street. The original station and yard, formally opened on 15 September 1830, were immediately east of the Water Street bridge, and thus above street level. The passenger departure platform was on the south side of the railway, with a frontage to Liverpool Road, where the two-storey reception building, still standing though in indifferent condition, incorporates a staircase from the main doorway up to rail level and a covered timber passenger 'platform' at rail level.

Opposite, on the north side of the line, also still standing but in indifferent condition, was the first goods shed, of a rhomboidal plan to suit the street pattern. Growth of traffic required rapid expansion of the station, particularly for goods traffic, and the 1849 1:500 Ordnance Survey plan shows an extensive system of specialised goods sheds, extending eastwards towards Lower Byrom Street and northwards to Grape Street. Later extensions, in the second half of the century, brought the railway and sheds up to Lower Byrom Street, where the rising ground meets rail level. The layout on the 1849 plan included as many as 64 wagon turntables, not only for right-angle or near right-angle turns into the goods sheds but also deputising for short turnouts in crossover roads. At the date of the survey the rhomboidal shed was specialising in butter, groceries, spirits and corn.

At the end of 1837 the passenger station was enlarged by an eastward extension alongside Liverpool Road, including a booking office for the Grand Junction Company, and also by the addition of an 'arrival station', of which little is now known, though it appears to have been on the north side of the railway and west of Water Street. On 4 May 1844 passenger trains ceased to use Liverpool Road on the completion of the connecting line to Victoria Station. Thence until 1972 Liverpool Road was a goods station, the agent's office being in the original passenger station, now a listed building and bearing a plaque unveiled in 1930 by the Lord Mayors of Manchester and Liverpool to commemorate its centenary. The old station is now being developed by stages as a museum of industrial archaeology, including railways.[7]

17. Old Main Goods Warehouse, Liverpool Road Station, Manchester   (HEW 955)   SJ 830 979

This must surely be the oldest surviving railway goods warehouse in the world; it is also one of the largest of the original Liverpool and Manchester Railway structures to remain. It is a simple structure deriving from a lengthy series of similar buildings used on inland waterways. Perhaps its very simplicity is remarkable; other warehouses described in these pages are monumental or highly architectural and this has influenced their survival.

The warehouse at Liverpool Road does have character, and size. It is a long narrow building approximately 350 ft by 60 ft on a curve, with three storeys, two above rail and one at street level. It is of brick with stone casings to the doorways and it has ten gables, that is ten separate transverse roofs above stout masonry partition walls. The floors, beams and columns are of wood, carefully designed to spread the load as well as possible. It has historical interest as it was used for the reception and cold collation on arrival of the inaugural train from Liverpool.

18. Grape Street Warehouse   (HEW 956)   SJ 831 979

The Liverpool Road railway terminal has included many sheds and warehouses in its long history. Two were destroyed by fire in 1866 and the present Grape Street building was a replacement. It is a neat and compact structure of six storeys, (four above rail level) and showing eight windows and four hoist openings on its main elevation. Inside there are three rows of eight columns supporting 16 in H-section beams lengthwise and 14 in ones crosswise with wood floors. There is a twin hipped roof with queen post composite trusses.

It is an excellent example of its period and forms, with HEWs 955 and 957, a unique set of three, namely the oldest, middle and newest railway warehouse all visible from the same spot.

19. Deansgate goods warehouse, Manchester   (HEW 957)
SJ 835 978

The third and most recent, and the largest, of the three railway warehouses in the Liverpool Road area is a part of the ex-Great Northern Railway's Deansgate Goods Terminal (no longer in use as such).

It is a very large and relatively modern structure opened in 1898.[8] It was built by Robert Neill and Sons of Manchester with steelwork by Heenan and Froude (Newton Heath), Sir William Arrol (Glasgow) and Keay and Sons (Darlaston) and hydraulic handling equipment by Sir William Armstrong Whitworth and Co. The Resident Engineer was W.T. Foxlee on behalf of successive chief engineers of the Great Northern Railway, namely Richard Johnson and Alexander Ross.

The building is 267 ft long by 217 ft wide by 75 ft high above street level, originally two goods sheds, one above the other, with three warehouse floors above. It is built of red brick, banded with blue, and has fireproof floors on steel columns and beams. It had rail and road access on two levels and connection below via a feeder—the erstwhile Manchester and Salford Junction Canal—to the Manchester Ship Canal.

The Great Northern Railway acted as outlet to London and the south for the Manchester, Sheffield and Lincolnshire Railway until the latter decided to built its own London extension and became the Great Central Railway. The Great Northern Railway then decided to have its own major depot in Manchester with access from the tracks of the Cheshire Lines Committee.

20. Victoria Station, Manchester   (HEW 521)   SJ 841 990
Within ten years of the opening of the Liverpool and Manchester Railway, developments elsewhere, notably the London and

Figure 8/5. Liverpool Road Station, Manchester (City of
Manchester, Local History Library)

Figure 8/6. Marple Aqueduct

Birmingham Railway and the projected Manchester and Leeds Railway, determined the future of Liverpool Road Station. Alternative schemes were considered and even favoured, but the opening of the Manchester and Bolton to Salford in 1838 and the Manchester and Leeds Railway to Oldham Road in 1839–41 led to an Act of 14 June 1839 for a new station at Hunts Bank (renamed Victoria) and another of 30 July 1842 for the Liverpool and Manchester Railway to link up with it. Trains were diverted at Miles Platting from Oldham Road to Hunts Bank on 1 January 1844 and the link was opened on 4 May 1844. There was one through common platform. Bolton trains were added from October 1846.

The west end eventually developed as part of the London and North Western Railway Exchange Station and the east end as the Lancashire and Yorkshire Railway Victoria Station. An even longer joint platform emerged in 1929 when platforms 3 and 11 became common to both stations, having an overall length of 2238 ft.

Victoria Station was extended southward towards Corporation Street in 1864. The plaques on the columns to the span between platforms 11 and 7 show 'W. Mabon, Ardwick Iron Works, Manchester'. The trusses of about 150 ft span have arched top booms and combined ties with ten bays of cross braced verticals, a less advanced form than in Liverpool Lime Street (HEW 103). Further extensions north and south in 1844 and 1904 gave Victoria a total of 17 platforms with further roofs.

21. Piccadilly (London Road) station roof, Manchester
(HEW 451)   SJ 848 978

In pre-nationalisation days this station was part of the London and North Eastern Railway (Great Central Railway), arising from the 1845 Manchester–Sheffield line via Woodhead, and the Manchester–Birmingham line.

Originally called Store Street, it became London Road in 1846 and Piccadilly about a century later. A major rebuild of roof took place in 1881 and there are now four spans of roof of 80–100 ft supported on lattice girders on cast iron columns, two lines of single and one of twin.

The trusses, like those at Victoria Station and Liverpool Lime Street have curved top booms and combined ties, the bracing being N-type (X at centre).

22. Manchester Central Station Roof   (HEW 450)
SJ 837 977

Disused for railway purposes since 5 May 1969 this terminus has
by far the most impressive roof structure of all the Manchester
Stations, and is exceeded in span only by St Pancras, of all British
Rail stations.

Built in 1880 and similar in design to St Pancras it has a span of
210 ft and a rise of 90 ft. The 16 ribs are curved Warren girders
about 4 ft 3 in deep. The contract drawings are signed by Andrew
Handyside (contractors of Derby), and Charles Sacre, A. Johnston,
and Richard Johnson, though the design was by Sir John Fowler.

Central Station is not far from Deansgate Goods Station and the
Liverpool Road area.

23. Croal Viaduct, Bolton   (HEW 251)   SD 722 093

This viaduct carries a railway over a road (now a dual carriageway),
a river (culverted) and a canal (filled in). It was designed by Charles
Vignoles, and built in 1847. Its four main arches are of cast iron,
and have a skew span of 76 ft and a rise of 13 ft. There are six ribs
each in three segments. Their design is simple, with plain verticals
in the spandrels, and transverse bracing tie rods and barrel struts.
The other six arches of the viaduct were built as segmental stone
arches, with spans of 36 ft and 12 ft rise. Two of the masonry piers
have been strengthened at springing level with steel collars. The
ironwork was by Ogle and Son of Preston.

24. March Barn Bridge, Rochdale Canal   (HEW 370)
SD 886 110

The original survey and estimates for the Rochdale Canal were
made by John Rennie, though he had little to do with the scheme
after that. The final survey for the route was made by William
Crossley, and the canal was designed by William Jessop, the
Resident Engineer being Crossley, who was succeeded by Thomas
Townshend. One of the contractors involved is known to have
been John Gilbert.

March Barn Bridge carries a road across the canal at a skew angle
of 60°. The bridge was completed in 1797, and the canal was
opened in two sections on different dates in 1798. The most
interesting feature about March Barn Bridge, apart from its skew, is
that the stones forming the voussoirs of the single arch span were

laid in winding courses. This difficult form of construction called for a high degree of skill on the part of the stone masons who built the bridge. The bridge is reckoned to be the oldest masonry skew arch in this country.

25. Marple Aqueduct   (HEW 26)   SJ 955 900   Figure 8/6

Benjamin Outram built this aqueduct in 1800 to carry the Peak Forest Canal over the River Goyt. The canal, connected Whaley Bridge with the Ashton Canal at Dukinfield 15 miles to the north. The aqueduct is situated at the foot of a flight of 16 locks which are themselves crossed by two small bridges. It has three 60 ft semi-circular arches of solid masonry with pierced spandrels and is about 90 ft high. The lower halves of the piers are in rough stone with rounded ends. The upper piers have narrow and graceful pilasters, each with a curved batter. There is a good view of this famous aqueduct from the adjacent railway viaduct and it will be seen that the well known 1863 engraving, although impressive, scarcely does it justice. The canal is now disused except for pleasure purposes.

26. Brabyns Park Bridge, Marple   (HEW 828)   SS 963 902

A rather different crossing of the River Goyt is the neat and attractive cast iron arch bridge in Brabyns Park, made in 1813 by Salford Iron Works. The three ribs span 50 ft in two segments. The spandrels carry the diminishing ring pattern, the rise is about 1 in 11 and the width 12 ft. There is a post and three-rail parapet fence with central motif carrying the letter W above the date. The masonry abutments and pilasters are of distinctive design.

27. Stockport Viaduct   (HEW 569)   SJ 891 903

Immortalised by L.S. Lowry but tending to be hidden by modern building developments, this viaduct is 1792 ft long and 110 ft high where it crosses the River Mersey in the centre of Stockport. It was completed in 1842 for the Manchester and Birmingham Railway. The designer was G.W. Buck, a former Resident Engineer for the construction of the London and Birmingham Railway, and the author of a treatise on oblique bridges. The viaduct has 26 arches (22 of equal 63 ft span) and is constructed mainly of brick with stone features at the base of the piers; the cost was £72 000. The same dimensions and form of construction were retained when the viaduct was widened in 1890 to accommodate four tracks. Centering and scaffolding used during the original construction were re-used for Dane Viaduct some 15 miles to the south on the same line.[9]

28. Dane Viaduct   (HEW 887)   SJ 772 679
Known also as Holmes Chapel Viaduct, this carries the railway over the River Dane on 23 arches of 63 ft span in red brick with stone facings, not far from Jodrell Bank Radio Telescope.

29. Runcorn Railway Bridge   (HEW 196)   SJ 509 835
Figure 8/7
This important structure was built in 1868 to carry the London and North Western Railway across the River Mersey. Hitherto the route from London to Liverpool was via Warrington, Earlestown, and the Liverpool and Manchester Railway. The river is crossed by three main spans of 305 ft formed by wrought iron double-web lattice girders supported on stone piers. The overhead lattice bracing to the top flange is masked by stone portals which (perhaps unfortunately) are surmounted by castellated turrets in the Victorian Gothic revival style reaching to 50 ft above rail level. These 'fortifications' are very fine in their way but unlike the essential structure they serve no useful purpose and are outmoded. The bridge carries the railway 75 ft above the river to allow sufficient headroom for ships passing beneath. In order to achieve such a height in the approach to the bridge, the railway is carried on 59 brick arches on its rise to the Widnes end of the bridge. The Engineer was William Baker and the contractor Thomas Brassey.[10] Just upstream of this bridge stands the elegant steel arch bridge built in 1961 to replace the Transporter Bridge, which has since been demolished. The latter was built in 1905 and was the longest (1000 ft span) and lowest (75 ft) of the four in this country.

30. Transporter Bridge, Warrington   (HEW 140)
SJ 597 877
Joseph Crosfield built his first soapworks in 1814 at Bank Quay, Warrington, beside the River Mersey. A modern chemical factory still stands on the same site. In 1914 a transporter bridge was built to carry goods across the river to the works. It was designed by

W.H. Hunter, built by Sir William Arrol, and opened in 1915. The bridge consists of a tower on either bank which is carried by mass concrete cellular foundations. Double cantilevers on each tower support a suspended central span, and the whole structure is built out of riveted mild steel plates and angles, with extensive use being made of laced and battened members. The car was originally designed to carry rail traffic of up to 18 tons in weight, and it was modified in 1940 to take road traffic as well. Further modifications in 1950 increased its capacity to 30 tons, and increased its length to its present overall length of 339 ft. The structure is 30 ft wide, and has a clearance of 76 ft at high water level. It has a clear span of 200 ft between the towers.

The two other remaining transporter bridges in this country are at Middlesbrough (see Chapter 3) and at Newport, Gwent.

31. Bridgewater Canal   (HEW 976)   SD 749 005

In addition to the transporter bridge there are other movable bridges in this area, some of them with unusual features. The most notable is that at Barton carrying the Bridgewater Canal over the Manchester Ship Canal.

Following the opening of the Sankey Brook Canal in 1757, the third Duke of Bridgewater decided to build a canal from his mines at Worsley to carry coal to Manchester, and it was first authorised by an Act of 1759. Originally it was proposed to lock down to the River Irwell at Barton, but the scheme was amended by an Act of 1760 to allow the canal to cross that river by a three-arch stone bridge, 39 ft above it, and to continue to Castlefield, Manchester, all on one level. This first section was opened on 17 July 1761, and it halved the cost of coal in Manchester. The Engineers were James Brindley and John Gilbert.

From the terminal basin at Worsley a system of 46 miles of underground canals penetrated into the workings of the Duke's collieries under Walkden and Farnworth. These collieries, now worked out, still drain into the canal causing discoloration for a mile each side of Worsley giving rise to the expression 'ochrey water' (local pronunciation 'ockry').

By 1722 the canal had been extended via Lymm to Runcorn (SJ 504 831) and later it was linked to the Trent and Mersey Canal (opened 1777) at Preston Brook (SJ 567 810), to the Rochdale Canal at Castlefield, and to the Leeds and Liverpool Canal at

Figure 8/7. Runcorn Railway Bridge (British Rail)

Figure 8/8. Barton Aqueduct (Manchester Ship Canal Co. Ltd)

Leigh, making it a vital link in the canal network of the north west. Apart from the flight down to the River at Runcorn, it had only one lock.

The replacement of the Barton aqueduct by a unique swing bridge in 1893 is dealt with in the next item. Of the old structure little remains: only the north abutment, a retaining wall and some arch stones re-erected alongside Barton Lane. Later developments included the repeated raising of the canal in the Worsley area to maintain water level despite subsidence of the surrounding land.

Commercial traffic ceased in 1974, but pleasure cruising, including sightseeing trips from the attractive packet-boat steps at Worsley, is booming. The Worsley complex includes graving docks which are still in use. Mining has ceased, but the National Mining Museum is being established at the recently closed Astley Green Colliery, 2½ miles west of Worsley, alongside the canal.

32. Barton Aqueduct   (HEW 28)   SJ 767 976
Figure 8/8

At Barton the Manchester Ship Canal occupies the site of the River Irwell and Brindley's fixed aqueduct had as a result to be replaced by a movable bridge.

The engineers, E.L. Williams, J. Abernethy and W.H. Hunter, designed a swing aqueduct which opens to permit the passage of vessels on the ship canal, and closes to allow traffic to pass along the Bridgewater Canal. The swing span consists of an iron trough 18 ft wide by 7 ft deep and 235 ft long which holds 1500 tons of water. This is supported on girders carried by main steel N-type twin girders. The aqueduct swings about its centreline which is on an island 400 ft by 30 ft. This also carries a road swing bridge. Before the aqueduct is moved the ends of the trough are closed by gates sealed by rubber wedges. The total weight of the swinging structure is 1600 tons.

The contractors were C.J. Wills for the substructure, Andrew Handyside for the iron work and Armstrong Mitchell and Co. for the machinery.

33. Manchester Ship Canal   (HEW 88)
SJ 369 811 to SJ 820 970

This 36 mile long ship canal is one of the most important civil engineering projects of the late Victorian era. It took six years to construct, and was opened in 1894.[11,12] It connects the estuary of the River Mersey with the new docks built at Salford near the heart of the City of Manchester. There are five sets of locks on the canal, the first being the entrance locks at Eastham, and they give a total rise of 56 ft 6 in. For most of its length the navigation channel is 120 ft wide and 28 ft deep. The canal cost over £15 million, and involved the excavation of 54 million yd³ of earth and rock. At the peak of activity 17 000 people were employed on its construction. A wide variety of mechanical plant was also used including 58 steam navvies, as well as cranes and railway locomotives and wagons.

The canal makes use of the River Irwell at the Manchester end and there are locks at Mode Wheel and Barton (to the west of the Bridgewater Canal Aqueduct). Near Irlam Locks the River Mersey is used, but from Thelwall on the M6 past Latchford Locks and south of Warrington the canal follows the left bank of the Mersey in a separate channel as far as Eastham.

The west coast main line railway (then the London and North Western Railway) was diverted westward on to a new high level bridge (by W. B. Farr) with severe gradients north and south. Parts of the old railway can still be seen on the up side. The two large bridges at Runcorn already described are also used by the canal as well as the river.

The Engineer was E. Leader Williams and there were numerous contractors.

34. Wallasey Embankment   (HEW 271)
SJ 241 911 to SJ 267 921

Beyond Eastham lies Birkenhead, across the Mersey from Liverpool, and north of Birkenhead is Wallasey which, with Bootle opposite, marks the end of the river.

The coastline of the Wirral between Wallasey and Hoylake, that is between the Mersey and the Dee, is low lying particularly in the central portion. It needs protection from the sea not only to prevent flooding of the hinterland but to protect the Port of Liverpool which would be devastated if major erosion allowed the Mersey to form two exit channels.

Moreover evidence suggests that this part of the Wirral is sinking at a rate of 3 ft every 100 years. In 1794 a 'slope wall or pavement' was built between Wallasey and Hoylake to reinforce the sand dunes. Made from local sand, clay, silt and peat, it was only partially successful.

In 1829 a 1.65 mile structure known as the 'old embankment' was built at a cost of £32 000. Its seaward slope varied between 1 in 4 and 1 in 8, and it was faced with 2 ft of local clay, which was later armoured with sandstone blocks. The square blocks varied in size from 8 in to 18 in and they were laid dry in bonded courses. Continuous maintenance was necessary, and in 1894 extensions were built at either end called the 'new embankment', bringing the total length of the structure to 2¼ miles at a cost of £16 370. A toe wall to prevent undercutting was built at a later date.

In 1941 the structure was faced with concrete about 6 in deep, the concrete being laid in a cellular pattern, the cells being about 13 ft square. However, the 19th century sandstone blocks stood up to the weather better than the 20th century concrete, and the passage of time inevitably meant that the structure has had to have major rebuilding done to it. This rebuilding started in 1973[13].

Bibliography and references

General Bibliography

ADAMSON S.H. *Seaside piers.* Batsford, London, 1977

BEAVER P. *A history of lighthouses.* Peter Davies, London, 1971

BLOWER A. *British railway tunnels.* Ian Allan, London, 1964

BREES S.C. *Railway practice,* 2nd series. John Williams, London, 1840

British Bridges. Public Works, Roads and Transport Congress, London, 1933

CODRINGTON T. *Roman roads in Britain.* Society for Promoting Christian Knowledge, London, 1919

COLEMAN T. *The railway navvies.* Hutchinson, London, 1965

COSSONS N. *The BP book of industrial archaeology.* David & Charles, Newton Abbot, 1975

CRESY E. *Encyclopaedia of civil engineering.* Longman, London, 1856

DOW G. *Great Central.* Locomotive Publishing Co. Ltd, London, 1959–65

FAIRBAIRN W. *The application of cast iron and wrought iron to building purposes.* Weale, London, 1857

HADFIELD C. *The canals of Yorkshire and North East England.* David & Charles, Newton Abbot, 1972

HADFIELD C. and BIDDLE G. *The canals of North West England.* David & Charles, Newton Abbot, 1970

HAGUE D. B. and CHRISTIE R. *Lighthouses: their architecture, history and archaeology.* Gomer Press, Llandysul, 1975

HOOLE K. *A regional history of the railways of England.* Vol. IV North Eastern England. David & Charles, Newton Abbot, 1965

HUMBER W. *Cast-iron and wrought-iron bridges and girders for railway structures.* Spon, London, 1857

JERVOISE E. *The ancient bridges of the North of England.* The Architectural Press, London, 1931

JOHNSON R.W. *The making of the Tyne.* Walter Scott Ltd., Newcastle Upon Tyne, 1895

LEECH Sir, B. *History of the Manchester Ship Canal.* Sherratt & Hughes, Manchester and London, 1907

MARGARY I.D. *Roman roads in Britain,* Phoenix House Ltd., London, 1957

MARSHALL C.F.D. *A centenary history of the Liverpool and Manchester Railway.* Locomotive Publishing Co. Ltd., London, 1930

MARSHALL J. *The Lancashire and Yorkshire Railway.* David & Charles, Newton Abbot, 1969, Vol 3

PRICE J. Movable bridges. *Proc. Instn Civ. Engrs,* 1879, **57**, March, 1–76

PRIESTLEY J. *Navigable rivers, canals and railways throughout Great Britain.* Longman, London, 1831

REED B. *Crewe to Carlisle.* Ian Allan, London, 1969

SMITH N. *A history of dams.* Peter Davies, London, 1971

STEEL W. L. The history of the London and North Western Railway. *Railway and Travel Monthly*, London, 1914

TOMLINSON W.W. *The North Eastern Railway*. Longmans Green, London, 1914 (reprinted David & Charles, Newton Abbot, 1967)

WALMISLEY A.T. *Iron roofs*. Spon, London, 1888

WALTERS D. *British railway bridges*. Ian Allan, London, 1963

WHISHAW F. *The railways of Great Britain and Ireland*. Simpkin Marshall, London, 1840 (reprinted David & Charles, Newton Abbot, 1969)

WRYDE J.S. *British lighthouses*. Unwin, London, 1913

Chapter 1: Border Country

1.	SMEATON J. *Reports of the late John Smeaton, FRS*. Longman, London, 1812, 2, 324–325

2.	IBID, 3, 235–251

3.	BRUCE G.B. Description of the Royal Border Bridge over the River Tweed on the York, Newcastle and Berwick Railway. *Proc. Instn Civ. Engrs*, 1851, 10, Feb., 219–244

4.	*A short history of Redpath Brown*. Redpath Brown Ltd., London, 1964

5.	ARTHUR B. Reinstatement: Union Chain Bridge. *Consult. Engr.*, 1976, 40, Feb., 27–28

Chapter 2: Tyne and Wear

1.	STURGESS R.W. An aristocrat in business. Durham County Local History Society, Durham, 1975

2.	GASK P.T. The construction of Seaham Harbour dock-works. *Proc. Instn Civ. Engrs*, 1905, 165, March, 252–261

3.	HARRISON T.E. On the Tyne docks at South Shields; and the mode adopted for shipping coals. *Proc.Instn Civ.Engrs*, 1859, 18, May, 490–524

4.	BROOKS W.A. Memoir on the River Tyne, *Proc. Instn Civ. Engrs*. 1867, 26, April, 398–441

5.	MESSENT P.J. Concrete work for harbours: discussion. *Proc. Instn Civ. Engrs*, 1886, 87, Nov., 148-152

6.	LINSLEY S.M. *Ryhope pumping station. A history and description*. Ryhope Engines Trust, Newcastle upon Tyne, 1973

7.	LAWSON W. The construction of the military road in Northumberland, 1751–57. *Archaeol.Aeliana*, Newcastle Upon Tyne, 1973, 5th Series, 1, 177–193

8.	SMEATON J. *Reports of the late John Smeaton, FRS*. Longman, London, 1812. 3, 267–344

9.	HOLMES H. The Roman bridge across the North Tyne river near Chollerford. *Archaeol.Aeliana*, Newcastle Upon Tyne, 1904, New Series, 16, 328–338

10.	BURR N. First rail bridge is stablised by resin grout system. *New Civ. Engr*, 1978, Feb., No. 281, 18–19

11.	GREEN B. On the arched timber viaducts on the Newcastle and North Shields Railway. *Proc. Instn Civ. Engrs*, 1846, 5, Feb., 219–232

12.	BOOTH L.G. Laminated timber arch bridges. *Trans.Newcomen Soc.*, 1971, 44, Oct., 1–21

13. BREMNER R.D. Account of the Victoria Bridge, erected across the River Wear, on the line of the Durham Junction Railway. *Proc. Instn Civ. Engrs*, 1843, **2**, Feb., 97–99

14. CUDWORTH W. The Hownes Gill viaduct on the Stockton and Darlington Railway. *Proc. Instn Civ. Engrs*, 1862, **22**, Nov., 44–57

15. The central Railway Station Newcastle upon Tyne. *Civ. Engr Arch. Jnl*, 1848, **11**, Dec., 353–354; 1849, **12**, April, 97

16. LAFFAN B.N. Notes upon the High Level Bridge at Newcastle. Reports of the Commissioners of Railways for the year 1849. *Rep. from Commis.*, 12, 1850. Appendix, 83–85

17. DAVIS F.W. and KIRKPATRICK C.R.S. The King Edward VII Bridge at Newcastle on Tyne, *Proc. Instn Civ. Engrs*, 1908, **174**, Apr. 158–221

18. ANDERSON D. Tyne Bridge, Newcastle. *Proc. Instn Civ. Engrs*, 1930, **230**, March, 167–202

19. LAWS W.G. Railway bridge over the River Tyne at Wylam, Northumberland. *Proc. Instn Civ. Engrs*, 1879, **56**, 262–274

20. GROVES G.L. The new Wearmouth Bridge, Sunderland. *Proc. Instn Civ. Engrs*, 1930, **230**, March, 144–165

Chapter 3: County Durham and Cleveland

1. SEMMENS P.W.B. *Exploring the Stockton and Darlington Railway*. Frank Graham, Newcastle, 1975

2. STOREY J. Description of the oblique bridge over the River Gaunless on the Hagger Leases branch railway, Durham. *Proc. Instn Civ. Engrs*, 1845, **4**, Jan., 59–61

3. The transporter bridge over the River Tees. *Engineer*, 1911, **112**, Sept., 336–337

4. HAMILTON J.A.K. and GRAVES J.T. Tees (Newport) Bridge, Middlesbrough, *Proc. Instn Civ. Engrs*, 1935, **240**, April, 567–617

Chapter 4: York and North Yorkshire

1. MARGARY I.D. *Romman roads in Britain*. Phoenix House, London, 1957, 2, 156–158

2. WHITWELL, J.B. The Church Street Sewer and an adjacent building. In ADDYMAN P.V. [ed.] *The archaeology of York*, **3**, no. 1. Council for British Archaeology, London, 1976

3. BUCKLAND P.C. The environmental evidence for the Church St Roman sewer system. *Ibid.*, **14**, 1

4. MacGREGOR A. Finds from a Roman sewer system and an adjacent building in Church St. *Ibid.*, **17**, 1

5. DOWRICK D.J. and BECKMANN P. York Minster structural restoration. *Proc. Instn Civ. Engrs*, 1971, Suppl. 6, 93–156 and 1972, Suppl. 11, 227–237

6. RANKIN S. and THOMPSON D. York 100, 1877–1977. British Railways Board, Eastern Region, York, 1977

Chapter 5: Cumbria

1. BIDWELL H.S. The outer barrier, Hodbarrow iron mines, Millom, Cumberland. *Proc. Instn Civ. Engrs*, 1906, **165**, March, 156-218

2. BRUNLEES J. Descriptions of the iron viaducts erected across the tidal estuaries of the Rivers Kent and Leven in Morecambe Bay for the Ulverstone and Lancaster Railway. *Proc. Instn Civ. Engrs*, 1858, **17**, April, 442–445

3. ALEXANDER J. Reconstruction of Kent and Leven viaducts, Furness section of the LM & S Railway. *Proc. Instn Civ. Engrs*, 1930, **230**, March, 125–142

4. TUPLIN W.A. *North Western steam*. George Allen and Unwin, London, 1963, 208.

5. MITCHELL W.R. and JOY D. *Settle and Carlisle Railway*. Dalesman Books, Clapham, N.Yorks, 1967

6. WILLIAMS F.S. *Midland Railway*. Strahan, London, 1876, 478–543

7. SANDERS E.M. Notable railway stations and their traffic. Carlisle (Citadel), London Midland and Scottish Railway. *Rlwy Mag.,* 1923, **52**, June, 431–438

8. CARMICHAEL J.G. and BLACKMORE J. *Views on the Newcastle and Carlisle Railway*. Currie and Bowman, Newcastle upon Tyne, 1836–8

9. MacLEAN J.S. *The Newcastle and Carlisle Railway*. Robinson, Newcastle upon Tyne, 1948

10. WILSON P. The Nent Force Level. *Trans. Cumb. Westmorland Antiqu. Archaeol. Soc.*, 1963, **63**, 253–280

11. The Manchester Thirlmere Waterworks. *Engineer*, Lond., 1894, **78**, Oct. 340–1, 375–7, 479–80; 1895, **79**, Jan., 46–47

12. HILL G.H. The Thirlmere Works for the water supply of Manchester. *Proc. Instn Civ. Engrs*, 1896, **126**, April, 2–23

13. TAYLOR G. The Haweswater Reservoir. *J. Instn Wat. Engrs*, 1951, **5** July, 355–399

Chapter 6: South and West Yorkshire

1. LEE C.E. The steam locomotive in 1812. *Rlwy Mag.*, 1962, **108**, June, 426–248

2. YOUELL S.M. The third century at Middleton. *Rlwy Mag.*, 1961, **107**, April, 223–229

3. ARMSTRONG Sir W.G. Description of the hydraulic swing bridge for the North Eastern Railway over the River Ouse near Goole. *Proc. Instn Mech. Engrs*, 1869, Aug., 121–132

4. CASTLE J.H. Municipal works at Goole. *Proc. Instn Mun. Engrs*, 1928, **55**, Sept., 605–606

5. TRIFFITT J. Swing bridge at Selby, North Eastern Railway. *Proc. Instn Civ. Engrs*, 1896-97, 128, 207-221

6. BRAY W.B. Description of the Ouse Bridge on the Hull and Selby Railway. *Proc. Instn Civ. Engrs*, 1845, **4**, Feb., 86–90

7. WALKER J. On ventilating and lighting tunnels. *Trans. Instn Civ. Engrs*. 1836, **1**, 95–98

8. ROLT L.T.C. Thomas Newcomen, *The prehistory of the steam engine*. David & Charles, Dawlish, 1963, 139

9. CLAYTON A.K. The Newcomen type engine at Elsecar. *Trans. Newcomen Soc.*, 1963, **35**, May, 97–108

10. SCOTT P.A. and CAMPBELL J.I. Woodhead new tunnel. *Proc. Instn Civ. Engrs*, Part 1, 1954, **3**, March, 506–563

11. BALGARNIE Rev. R. *Sir Titus Salt (Bart.)* Hodder and Stoughton, London, 1877. Reprinted Brenton Publishing Co. Settle, 1970

12. LINSTRUM D. *Historic architecture of Leeds*. Oriel Press, Leeds, 1969

13. CHADWICK S. *Gateway to the south*. Venturer's Press, Huddersfield, 1950

14. HAWKSHAW J. Description of the Lockwood Viaduct on the Huddersfield and Sheffield Railway. *Proc. Instn Civ. Engrs*, 1850, **10**, April, 296–302

Chapter 7: Lancashire and the Isle of Man

1. Blackpool Tower. *Engineering*, London, 1895, **59**, May–June, 575, 660–662, 727–729, 786–791

2. BLACKPOOL PIER CO LTD. *The North Pier, Blackpool,* 1863-1913. Falkner, Manchester, 1913

3. HOOPER H. Description of the pier at Southport, Lancashire. *Proc. Instn Civ. Engrs*, 1861, **20**, March, 292–299

4. SMITH M.H. The Blackpool electric tramway. *Electrician*, 1886, **17**, Sept., 370–378

5. PHILLIPS D.F. The Blackpool and Fleetwood Tramroad Co, 1896–1920. *Tramwy Rev.*, 1958, **4**, No. 25, 2–29

6. MITCHELL A. On submarine foundations; particularly the screw pile and moorings. *Proc. Instn Civ. Engrs*, 1848, **7**, Feb., 108–146

7. DENHAM H.M. *Sailing directions from Point Lynas to Liverpool: supplement on Wyre and Port Fleetwood*. J. & J. Mawdsley, Liverpool, 1840

8. BUTLER R.B. *et al.* A history of the Marsh Mill, Thornton: measured study. *Architecture North West*, No. 4 1964, April–May, 87–90

9. BOYD J.I.C. *The Isle of Man Railway*. Oakwood Press, Lingfield, 1973

10. PEARSON F.K. *Isle of Man tramways*. David & Charles, Newton Abbot, 1970

11. HOSKING W. Constructions to retain the sides of deep cuttings. *Proc. Instn Civ. Engrs*, 1844, **3**, June, 355–374

Chapter 8: Merseyside and Greater Manchester

1. GREENSLADE R. Albert Dock, Liverpool: reinstatement. *Consult. Engr*, 1976, **40**, Feb., 22–25

2. LAKEMAN A. The Royal Liver Building, Liverpool. *Concrete Construc. Engng*, 1911, **6**, Oct., 727–735

3. BOOTH H. *An account of the Liverpool and Manchester Railway*. Wales & Baines, Liverpool, 1830

4. CARLSON R.E. *The Liverpool and Manchester railway project*. David & Charles, Newton Abbot, 1969

5. DONAGHY T.J. *Liverpool and Manchester operations, 1831–45*. David & Charles, Newton Abbot, 1972

6. TURNER R. Description of the iron roof over the railway station, Lime Street, Liverpool. *Proc. Instn Civ. Engrs*, 1850, **9**, Feb., 204–214

7. STOKER G.J. The oldest railway station in the world. *Rlwy Mag.*, 1902, **11**, Nov., 385–392

8. FOXLEE W.T. New Goods Station, Great Northern Railway, Manchester, *Engineer*, London, 1898, **86**, Sept., 224–225

9. BROWN W.E.S. Railways in 1841. *Rlwy Mag.*, 1922, **50**, April, 253

10. The Runcorn Bridge, *Engineer*, London, 1866, **21**, June, 472–473

11. WILLIAMS Sir E.L. *et al.* The Manchester Ship Canal. *Proc. Instn Civ. Engrs*, 1897, **131**, Nov., 14–99

12. The Manchester Ship Canal, *Engineering*, London, 1894, 57, Jan., 97–142
13. BELL M.N. *et al.* The Wallasey Embankment. *Proc. Instn. Civ. Engrs*, Part 1, 1975, 58, Nov., 569–590

Additional sites

Other sites of civil engineering interest, recorded or under investigation, are listed below.

Border Country
Drygrange road bridge, near Melrose NT 574 347

Canongate Bridge, Jedburgh NT 653 205

Kielder railway viaduct NY 632 924

Weldon ancient road bridge NZ 138 985

Coquet railway viaduct NU 222 038

Morwick water tower NU 239 036

Aln railway viaduct NU 229 121

Tyne and Wear
Killhope Wheel NY 827 429

Bothal railway viaduct NZ 215 865

Morpeth road bridge NZ 201 858

Plessey railway viaduct NZ 227 790

Seaton Sluice NZ 337 769

Whittle Dean reservoirs NZ 065 680

Whittle Dean to Newcastle water main NZ 074 673 to NZ 245 638

Corbridge ancient road bridge NY 989 641

Ovingham lattice girder bridge NZ 086 636

Newburn Bridge NZ 165 652

Glass-making cone (brick tower), Lemington NZ 184 646

Reinforced concrete granary, Dunston NZ 229 627

Victoria colliery tunnel, Newcastle NZ 236 654 to NZ 264 641

Chimney Windmill, Newcastle NZ 240 655

Robert Stephenson's works, Forth St, Newcastle NZ 247 637

Manor Chare Bridge, Newcastle NZ 253 641

Armstrong Bridge, Newcastle NZ 264 662

Cast iron arch bridge, North Shields NZ 359 688

Lambton ancient road bridge NZ 284 523

Chester-le-Street railway viaduct NZ 271 516

North Eastern Railway standard cast iron footbridge, Beamish Museum (ex-Dunston staithes) NZ 217 549

County Durham and Cleveland
Plawsworth railway viaduct NZ 271 477

Reinforced concrete footbridge, Kingsgate, Durham NZ 276 423

Relly Mill railway viaduct NZ 258 421

Croxdale railway viaduct NZ 263 376

Newton Cap railway viaduct NZ 206 303

Blackwell Bridge, Darlington NZ 270 126

Yarm railway viaduct NZ 417 130

Yarm ancient road bridge NZ 418 131

Victoria Bridge, Stockton NZ 449 183

Hartlepool Docks   NZ 51 33 to NZ 52 34

Saltburn Station roof   NZ 664 215

York and North-east Yorkshire
Sowerby Pack Horse Bridge, Thirsk SE 433 816

Cast iron arch bridge, Myton on Swale   SE 436 667

Cast iron foot bridge, Ripley, Harrogate   SE 283 606

Nidd railway viaduct, near Harrogate   SE 306 584

Tadcaster railway viaduct   SE 485 438

Skelton railway bridge, near York SE 565 553

Scarborough branch railway bridge over River Ouse, York   SE 596 521

Skeldergate Bridge, York   SE 603 512

Kexby ancient road bridge   SE 705 511

Filey Station roof   TA 114 807

Scarborough Harbour   TA 04 88

Esk Viaduct, Whitby   NZ 897 097

Cumbria
Whitehaven Harbour   NX 970 185

Maryport Lighthouse   NY 028 369

Lanercost ancient road bridge   NY 554 634

Lambley viaduct   NY 675 584

Eamont Bridge   NY 522 288

Blea Moor Tunnel   SD 761 819 to 775 838

Lune Railway viaduct, Ingleton SD 630 930

Lancaster Canal   SD 520 925 to 527 303

South and West Yorkshire
M62 Motorway, Pennine Section SD 944 135 to SE 114 195

Slaithwaite Dam   SE 075 141

Esholt sewage disposal works   SE 185 395

Arthington railway viaduct   SE 265 456

Kirkstall Viaduct, Leeds   SE 279 342

Crown Point Bridge, Leeds   SE 307 331

Shippen Lane cast iron arch bridge, Leeds & Selby Railway   SE 387 342

Fairburn cast iron arch bridge, York & North Midland Railway   SE 479 275

Crimple high viaduct   SE 530 320

Cawood swing bridge   SE 574 378

Walton Hall cast iron bridge, Wakefield   SE 363 163

Television Mast, Emley Moor   SE 222 130

Barugh railway viaduct   SE 318 090

Conisbrough railway viaduct   SK 525 994

Sheffield sewage disposal works SK 396 916

Palm House, Botanic Gardens, Sheffield   SK 334 863

Lancashire and the Isle of Man
Douglas Head Lighthouse, Isle of Man   SC 390 748

Fleetwood Docks   SD 33 47

Lytham Windmill   SD 349 341

Preston Station roof   SD 534 290

Entwistle Dam   SD 723 173

Abbeystead Dam   SD 557 538

Cowm Dam   SD 881 187

Hamer Pasture Dam   SD 896 162

Merseyside and Greater Manchester
Warrington Bridge (reinforced concrete arch)   SJ 608 879

Bradshaw Brook railway viaduct, Bolton   SD 727 171

Scowcroft Bridge, Manchester   SD 887 066

Stalybridge Aqueduct   SJ 954 982

Dove Stone Dam, Stalybridge   SE 014 036

Index